THE AUSTRALIAN
Women's Weekly
Diabetes

Delicious recipes that will have you happy to eat healthy

BAUER

MEDIA GROUP

CONTENTS

LET'S TALK DIABETES

Living with diabetes can be a struggle, what with planning meals, counting carbohydrates, recording blood sugar levels, etc. This book is designed to take the hassle out of mealtimes: the recipes, while developed specifically for diabetes, will suit any healthy lifestyle.

BUT FIRST, WHAT IS DIABETES?

Essentially, diabetes is an excess of glucose (sugar) in the blood caused by a lazy or low functioning pancreas. The pancreas produces a hormone called insulin, which moves glucose from the blood stream into muscles and cells where it is converted to energy. The pancreas of someone with diabetes either does not make enough insulin, or produces insulin that is unable to do the job that the body requires of it.

There are two main types of diabetes, type 1 and type 2.

Type 1

Type 1 diabetes is an autoimmune disease where insulin-producing cells in the pancreas have been destroyed by the immune system. Type 1 diabetes constitutes about 10-15% of all cases in Australia; it involves daily injections of insulin, and is commonly diagnosed during childhood and early adulthood.

There is no single known cause, but it is thought that some of us have a genetic disposition toward this condition; the idea is that when these people are exposed to a trigger, such as a viral infection, it triggers an autoimmune response that attacks the insulin-producing cells and type 1 diabetes develops as a result.

DISCLAIMER – The following information provides basic guidelines to healthy eating for people with diabetes. Please check with your doctor, dietitian or diabetes educator as to the suitability of this information for your diabetes management.

Type 2

Type 2 diabetes is largely caused by lifestyle factors and, these days, is vastly more common than type 1. Type 2 diabetes can affect people of all ages and represents between 85-90% of cases in Australia. It often develops gradually with symptoms such as blurred vision, skin infections, slow healing, tingling and numbness in the feet, although sometimes there may be no symptoms at all.

Type 2 diabetes occurs when the body no longer produces enough insulin, or when insulin is no longer working efficiently, to move glucose from the blood into the cells; this is known as insulin resistance.

Lifestyle factors that contribute to developing type 2 diabetes include a poor diet, limited exercise, smoking and being overweight. Other risk factors can be family background or suffering from a pre-diabetes condition such as hyperglycaemia where blood glucose levels are higher than they should be.

MANAGEMENT

Diabetes cannot be cured, but it can be managed. While genetics plays a part in the likelihood of someone developing type 2 diabetes, an unhealthy lifestyle is a major factor. This includes a particularly an unhealthy diet high in saturated fat (e.g. sausages, cheese, ice-cream, take-away food), low in fibre (i.e. lacking vegetables, fruit and wholegrain breads and cereals), high in kilojoules (from too much fat, sugar, alcohol and large-portion sizes).

It is important to manage diabetes with a good diet: 4-7 servings of high-fibre breads and cereal foods, at least 5 servings of vegetables, 2-3 servings of fruit, 2-3 servings of low-fat dairy products (including milk and yoghurt) 1-2 servings of lean protein (including meat, poultry, fish, legumes and nuts) and small amounts of good (unsaturated) fats spread across three meals. It is also important to undertake physical activity and to take medication as required.

VITAMIN D DEFICIENCY

This has recently been associated with the development of type 2 diabetes. The main source of vitamin D comes from exposure to sunlight. Foods containing vitamin D include oily fish (salmon, mackerel, sardines and herring), eggs and fortified foods (foods that have had vitamin D added to them such as margarine, milk and yoghurt). Vitamin D levels can be checked with a simple blood test and vitamin D supplements are readily available.

It is important to remember that everyone is at risk of diabetes; approximately 240 million people live with diabetes globally. This figure is likely to increase to 380 million by 2025.

The above diet recommendations are based on the following serving sizes

BREADS AND CEREALS	VEGETABLES	FRUIT	DAIRY PRODUCTS	LEAN PROTEIN
1 serving = 1 slice bread or ½ medium bread roll or ½ cup cooked rice/pasta/noodles or ½ cup cooked porridge or ¼ cup untoasted muesli or ⅔ cup high-fibre cereal.	1 serving = 1 cup salad or 75g cooked vegetables/legumes or 1 small potato.	1 serving = 1 medium piece of fruit (150g) or 1 cup diced fruit pieces or 1 cup drained canned fruit or ½ cup fruit juice.	1 serving = 1 cup (250ml) milk or 1 small carton (200g) yoghurt or 2 slices cheese.	1 serving = 65-100g cooked meat or 80-120g cooked fish fillet or 2 small eggs or ½ cup cooked legumes (eg beans, lentils, chickpeas) or ⅓ cup nuts.

IF IT ALL SOUNDS A BIT HARD...

WHAT HAPPENS IF YOU IGNORE DIABETES?

Uncontrolled diabetes or persistently high blood sugar (glucose) levels in both kinds of diabetes can wreak damage throughout the body, from your heart to your teeth to your kidneys. These are referred to as diabetes-related complications.

It's not all doom and gloom. A healthy active lifestyle can assist in the prevention and management of diabetes. Healthy lifestyles help us manage cholesterol, blood pressure and blood glucose levels and increase insulin sensitivity (that's a good thing) in addition to the assistance provided by insulin or other medication. Remember, if you have diabetes you should discuss any dietary changes with a medical professional first.

DIABETES COMPLICATIONS

VISION

Diabetic retinopathy, or damage to the retina caused by diabetes, is the leading cause of blindness for Australians aged under 60. The development of retinopathy strongly correlates with the length of time diabetes has been present and the extent to which blood glucose levels have been controlled. Regular tests and treatment can prevent blindness caused by retinopathy.

KIDNEY FUNCTION

Our kidneys filter our blood. They remove waste from the bloodstream that is passed out of the body through urine. Diabetes can damage the kidneys causing them to leak. Because this damage occurs over a period of time and often goes undetected, it usually goes unnoticed until it is quite advanced leaving sufferers with two options: dialysis or a kidney transplant. This is why it is important to have your kidney function checked annually. The kidneys are also affected by high blood pressure so it is a good idea to have this checked every three months too.

DEPRESSION

Living with diabetes isn't easy. It can be frustrating, tedious and painful. If living with a chronic illness wasn't bad enough, there is also the constant threat of developing the complications discussed here, such as damage to the eyes, nerves and kidneys. Diabetes may also increase the risk of developing depression. It's important that people diagnosed with diabetes have someone they can confide in, such as a health professional, family member, friend or colleague.

RECORD YOUR LIFESTYLE

Keep a record of your food intake, physical activity and blood glucose levels. This allows you to determine the impact of food, physical activity and your diabetes treatment (tablets/ or insulin) on your blood glucose levels (BGLs). If you notice your BGLs are elevated 2 hours after a meal:

1

Have you eaten more carbohydrates than usual? If so, reduce the amount eaten next time and measure your BGL to determine the impact.

2 Consider swapping high-GI carbohydrate foods for lower-GI options (see the section on Low-GI Food page 12).

3

Go for a walk. Exercise helps control your BGL, lowers blood pressure and reduces the risk of heart disease. Discuss exercising with your doctor.

4 Talk to your diabetes team; if the elevated BGL is not lifestyle related, it can be due to other problems such as illness or infection.

GET PHYSICAL

Current medical guidelines recommend that you should exercise for a minimum of 30 minutes every day. This includes a mixture of aerobic exercise, such as walking, and resistance exercise, such as lifting weights. Before starting an exercise regime, it is important to discuss any increase or change to your routine with your doctor or diabetes educator.

CIRCULATION

Neuropathy or peripheral nerve disease and vascular damage (damage to the blood vessels) may lead to decreased sensation in the lower limbs, leg ulcers and serious foot problems. This can lead to lower limb amputation. Personal daily foot checks and thorough annual foot examinations conducted by your doctor or podiatrist will help to reduce your risk of lower limb complications.

CARDIOVASCULAR AND BLOOD VESSEL DAMAGE

Diabetes affects the blood vessels. It increases the risk of heart disease and stroke associated with high blood glucose levels, high blood pressure and high cholesterol. High glucose levels can also increase the risk of infection, delay wound healing and increase the risk of gum disease.

Managing diabetes doesn't have to be boring; this book showcases a range of tasty recipes that will help keep healthy eating interesting.

GETTING STARTED

Not all carbohydrate foods are beneficial; less nutritious forms of carbohydrate-rich foods include chocolate, cakes, biscuits, pastries, lollies, regular ice-cream and soft drinks. These foods are high in fat and added sugar and should be treated as occasional foods only.

COUNTING CARBOHYDRATES

Carbohydrate is the best source of energy for the body. When carbohydrate-rich foods are digested, they are broken down to glucose. By eating regular meals, and spreading your carbohydrate foods evenly throughout the day, you will assist the body in maintaining constant energy levels; eat too much in one sitting and you will cause your blood glucose levels to spike. The quality of carbohydrate foods is equally as important as the quantity. Limit highly processed foods that don't provide much nutrition (white flour, white breads and breakfast cereals high in added sugar). Choose carbohydrate foods high in fibre and low in fat, as these tend to be excellent sources of fibre, vitamins and minerals. Around half of all kilojoules (or calories) should come from carbohydrate foods.

> As a protein and carbohydrate, legumes (beans, peas and lentils) are a tasty alternative to lean meat, poultry and fish, and rice, potato and pasta, and they have a low glycaemic index (GI).

CARBOHYDRATE RICH FOODS

• *Bread or bread rolls:* choose wholegrain, wholemeal, rye or fruit bread.

• *Breakfast cereals:* choose high-fibre varieties such as rolled oats, bran cereals or untoasted muesli.

• *Pasta, rice:* (basmati, doongara or brown) and other grains such as barley, burghul and couscous.

• *Starchy vegetables:* potatoes, sweet potato, sweet corn, yam, parsnip.

• *Legumes:* baked beans, kidney beans, chickpeas, lentils, three-bean mix.

• *Fruit:* all types such as apples, oranges, peaches, bananas, melons. Fruit is a good source of fibre.

• *Milk products or dairy alternatives:* choose low-fat varieties of milk, soy drink (calcium fortified), yoghurt.

• *High-fibre crispbreads.*

FAT

Fats have the highest kilojoule (or calorie) content of all nutrients. Eating too much fat may cause weight gain that in the long term poses a challenge to managing blood glucose levels. A healthy eating plan, which is lower in fat, particularly saturated fat, is advised to help prevent and manage type 2 diabetes.

SATURATED FAT

It is important to limit saturated fat because it raises total and LDL (bad) cholesterol levels. Saturated fat is also linked with insulin resistance. Saturated fat is found in animal foods such as fatty meat, full-fat dairy products, butter and cheese. It is also found in palm oil (found in solid cooking fats, snack and take-away foods) and coconut products such as copha, coconut milk or coconut cream. Quick substitutes include choosing tomato-based sauces rather than cream-based ones, or swapping processed meats, such as sandwich ham, with lean chicken.

FREE VEGETABLES

Non-starchy vegetables or 'free vegetables' are virtually carbohydrate and kilojoule free. This means they have limited or no impact on your blood glucose levels and weight. You can eat as many free vegetables as you like, including:

• artichoke	• celery	• radish
• asparagus	• cucumber	• salad
• broccoli	• eggplant	greens
• brussels	• green beans	• spinach
sprouts	• leek	• tomatoes
• cabbage	• lettuce	• zucchini
• capsicum	• mushroom	
• cauliflower	• onion	

GOOD FATS

Not all fats are bad, some are important for good health. Mono and polyunsaturated fats do not raise cholesterol levels. Eat a variety of polyunsaturated and monounsaturated fats to achieve a good balance. These include:

Monounsaturated fats – including olive oil, macadamias, avocados, peanuts, pecans, pistachios, almonds, cashews and hazelnuts.

Polyunsaturated fats – including walnuts, brazil nuts, pine nuts and oily fish, which also contain omega-3, as well as seeds and seed oils like sesame and safflower, which are also rich in omega-6.

SHOPPING ADVICE

• Never go food shopping when you are hungry.

• Make a shopping list and stick to it. This way no sneaky packets of chocolate biscuits or chips make their way into the trolley.

• Shop when you have plenty of time, so you can read the nutritional information on packages and reduce the chance you will make bad choices because you're in a hurry.

• Try to stick to the outside aisles of the supermarket. This is where you will find the fresh fruit, vegies, meat and dairy, and where you don't tend to find processed convenience foods.

HEALTHY SNACKS

The aim is to make meals that are full of flavour and colour and well-balanced for good health. If you enjoy a snack between meals, keep the snack small and select healthy options. Snacks are not required by everyone; speak to your dietitian for advice.

FRUITS

1 medium apple or pear or half a mango or 2 plums or 1 peach or 1 large slice of watermelon or half a rockmelon. Strawberries, raspberries, blackberries, blueberries, passionfruit and unsweetened rhubarb are free foods (ie you can eat as much of them as you like).

VEGETABLES

Vegetable sticks: celery, carrot, capsicum and snow peas.

NUTS

30g unsalted nuts such as cashews, walnuts or almonds.

BREADS

1 regular slice raisin or multigrain toast.

CEREAL

½ cup high-fibre breakfast cereal with ½ cup low-fat milk.

DRINKS

1 skim café latte or 1 cup (250ml) of a low-fat flavoured milk or soy milk or fruit smoothie.

CAKES

1 small pikelet or wholemeal crumpet or 1 small fruit or plain scone with 1 teaspoon jam.

DAIRY

200g tub of low-fat yoghurt.

SAVOURY

4 high-fibre crispbread biscuits or 3 rice cakes topped with cottage cheese, a slice of tomato and chives; half an english muffin with 1 slice reduced-fat cheese and a slice of tomato, or 2 pitta bread triangles, or a small can of baked beans.

ABOUT THE RECIPES

We provide the kilojoule content so you can stay within recommended energy intake guidelines.

Energy (kilojoules)
The average adult daily intake is around 8700 kilojoules; this is *average*, however, and daily energy intake requirements will vary among individuals depending on age, sex, body size, weight and activity level. It also depends on whether you are a child, pregnant or suffer a medical condition.

Total fat
Daily intake should be limited to 30-35 per cent of total kilojoules; that is, 40-50g of fat per day.

Saturated fat
Fat intake should be less than seven per cent of total daily kilojoule allowance; that is, less than 10g daily.

Carbohydrates
Daily intake should be 50-60 per cent of total kilojoules; that is, 200-250g per day. Use low-GI, high-fibre carbohydrate sources wherever possible.

Dietary fibre
Recommendations are 28g for women and 38g for men of dietary fibre daily.

Protein
Protein intake should be 10-15% of total daily kilojoules. The ideal intake should be no more than 80-100g per day. As a guideline, allow 1g of protein for each kg of your ideal body weight; ie an 80kg person should eat only 80g of protein a day.

EATING OUT

Don't feel that you can't go to restaurants and enjoy yourself. While this is one situation where you have minimal control on the size of the portion on your plate, and to a lesser extent, how the food is cooked, you can select wisely.

• For an entrée, *choose a salad-based dish, steamed vegetables or soup* instead of anything deep-fried.

• *Be aware* of your total carbohydrate intake and how it is prepared. *Be cautious* of chips or mashed potato, pasta, rice and breads that are prepared with butter, creamy sauces or cheese.

• *Select a salad* as the side dish or roasted or steamed vegetables without a cream-based sauce or butter. Ask if the chef will add ground black pepper and fresh lemon juice as a substitute.

• Some meals provide excess food. Consider asking for *a smaller portion*, or if you can order an entrée as the main course. Try sharing plates if the dishes are too large.

• When eating Italian food, *avoid heavy lasagnes and creamy pasta sauces.* Instead, select a dish with fresh tomato sauce. The same criteria applies to when dining in an Indian or classic French restaurant.

• When *faced with a buffet*, choose from the healthier foods. Keep in mind the limits of the carbohydrates for each serving. Always be mindful of how much you're eating.

• If they don't already know, *tell friends and relatives you have dietary requirements* if you're invited round for dinner. It saves you the embarrassment of saying no to food they have created for your visit, and the host being mortified that they cannot serve you the best meal for your health.

• Desserts can be oh-so tempting. *Fresh fruit and yoghurt are good choices.* A good restaurant will ask the chef to prepare a fruit platter fresh for you.

• *Drinks:* both men and women should not have more than two standard drinks a day (1 standard drink is equal to a middy (285ml) of beer, a small glass of wine (100ml) or a nip of spirits (30ml). It is also recommended that you have some alcohol-free days each week.

• Always choose the *wholegrain roll*.

• *No butter* on the roll.

It can be tempting to overeat at restaurants or friends' places, but there are a few helpful strategies that can assist you. One is to drink a large glass of water before leaving home; another is to have a small snack such as a small cup of soup or a small plate of leafy green salad (choose a low-fat dressing), so that you are not so hungry when it comes time to eat.

GLYCAEMIC INDEX FOODS

Not all carbohydrates are created equal. Low GI (Glycaemic Index) carbohydrates are unprocessed, complex carbohydrates that have terrific health benefits; they are digested and absorbed slowly by the body, so you will have more energy and feel satisfied for longer.

WHY IS GI IMPORTANT?

Most low-GI foods are based on high-fibre carbohydrates. The GI measures the process of carbohydrate digestion, absorption and release. Eating low-GI foods (GI less than or equal to 55) slows the rate of digestion and absorption, so they don't raise blood glucose levels too rapidly. Importantly for people with diabetes, low-GI foods help to maintain blood glucose levels. Select foods with a low-GI for meals and snacks. It is still important to watch your portions of low-GI foods, as too large a portion can still lead to increased BGLs; and remember not all low-GI foods are healthy everyday options.

Cooking methods

The method of cooking also affects the GI of food. If food is overcooked so that it is 'broken down' too much, it will have a higher GI than it would in its less-processed state, eg: mashed potato has a higher GI than boiled or baked potato; overcooked rice or pasta has a higher GI compared to if they are cooked al dente.

Help to lower the GI

• Add lentils, barley, split peas, haricot beans and pasta pieces to soups

• Add kidney or borlotti beans or lentils to soups and casseroles

• Add lentils, canned beans and even rolled oats to rissoles in combination with the meat base

• When it comes to breakfast cereals, use unprocessed rolled oats, oat bran, rice bran or lower-fat natural muesli.

LOW-GI FOODS

• *Fruit:* apples, apricots, bananas, cherries, grapefruit, grapes, kiwifruit, lemons, mandarins, mango, oranges, passionfruit, peaches, pears, plums.

Vegetables: cabbage, corn, carisma potato, kumara (orange sweet potato).

• *Legumes:* kidney, white and soya beans, chickpeas, lentils.

• *Pasta:* all pasta varieties are low-GI, but wholemeal varieties are better choices as they have a higher fibre, vitamin and mineral content.

• *Ice-cream:* look for low-GI and low-fat varieties.

• *Yoghurt* is best bought in the low-fat variety. No-added sugar is the better choice.

• *Milk:* low- or no-fat.

• *Jam:* look for 100% fruit or low-GI varieties and use without butter.

• *Vinegar and vinaigrette dressings:* can lower blood glucose levels by slowing the rate of food emptying from the stomach. Red or white wine vinegars are both good choices.

VISUAL REMINDER USING YOUR HAND – PER SERVING

PALM OF HAND

Portion of cooked fish, skinless chicken or lean meat.

FIST

Approximately 1 cup fresh fruit; 1 serving of low-fat milk or yoghurt.

THREE MIDDLE FINGERS TOGETHER

Size of potato.

LENGTH OF THUMB

Amount of low-fat salad dressing.

Amount of avocado.

TIP OF THUMB

Amount of unsaturated oil; amount of jam/vegemite/peanut butter.

Amount of unsaturated margarine.

CENTRE OF CUPPED PALM

(approximately 50c piece)

Amount of unsalted nuts; amount of reduced-fat cheese.

You can get plenty of information from your doctor or dietitian, as well as from the Australian Diabetes Council or the diabetes association in your country. Read all you can, then make a plan to help you manage your diabetes and maintain your lifestyle.

LOWER-GI PANTRY STAPLES

High-quality wholegrain bread (around 20 kibbled grains): whole or cracked grains – in baked goods use oat bran, rice bran or rolled oats instead of flour if suitable for the recipe.

Rice: use basmati, doongara, rather than jasmine or short-grain rice, or use pearl barley, buckwheat, bulgur, couscous or quinoa. Be aware that it's not the colour of the rice that determines its GI value: brown basmati rice will have a low-GI but other brown varieties probably won't.

Orange-fleshed sweet potato or kumara in preference to most varieties of white potato. Sweet potato is higher in fibre, which helps to slow the digestion and absorption of glucose into the blood. While some new varieties of white potatoes (see right) have a different ratio of starch, most are still considered to have a moderate-to-high GI.

Most varieties of white potatoes have a high GI because they contain large amounts of easily digested starches that produce a rapid rise in blood glucose levels. Nicola, Carisma and Almera are varieties of white potato with GI values similar to orange-fleshed sweet potato.

Note – The GI values we have given for the recipes in this book are estimates only.

WHAT'S ON A PLATE

The key to portion control is to downsize some foods and increase others to achieve a balanced plate. An easy way to judge this is to divide your plate into quarters. Roughly, one quarter should be carbohydrates, another quarter should be protein and two quarters should be vegetables.

Never pile food higher than a flat deck of cards. Diameter of inside rim of the plate is 20cm (8 inches).

Lean protein
65-100g chicken breast; fish fillet; or lean steak.

Free vegetables/salad
(eat as much as you like)
Lettuce, broccoli, broccolini, asparagus, celery, green beans, beetroot, tomatoes, cabbage, capsicum, cauliflower, cucumber, brussels sprouts, mushrooms, onion, leeks, spinach, squash, leafy salad mixes, zucchini, radish.

High-fibre/Lower-GI carbohydrate
Steamed couscous; pasta or rice (basmati or doongara); wholegrain bread; baked or mashed kumara (orange sweet potato); or fresh corn.

7-DAY MENU PLANNER

DAY	BREAKFAST	SNACK	LUNCH	SNACK	DINNER	DESSERT	TOTAL DAILY INTAKE
MONDAY	strawberry and passionfruit breakfast trifle (page 16)	¼ cup unsalted mixed nuts	spinach and cheese snails (page 55)	1 small banana	spanish pork cutlets (page 76)	coffee granita (page 106)	45.8g total fat (9.2g saturated fat); 5410kJ (1292 cal); 129.7g carbohydrate; 89g protein; 45g fibre; 1027mg sodium
TUESDAY	chia and almond toasted muesli (page 21)	invigorating fruit and vegetable juice (page 35)	vietnamese pancakes with prawns (page 61)	1 small apple	miso broth with salmon and soba (page 78)	frozen peach lassi (page 103)	44.1g total fat (8.4g saturated fat); 6630kJ (1585 cal); 196.1g carbohydrate; 78.6g protein; 28.5g fibre; 1424mg sodium
WEDNESDAY	toast with avocado, tahini and sumac tomatoes (page 32)	½ cup blueberries with 1 small (100g) tub low-fat fruit yoghurt	spiced lentil and roasted kumara soup (page 40)	2 medium kiwi fruit	grilled steak with salsa verde and soft polenta (page 89)	passionfruit mousse (page 101)	48.7g total fat (8.9g saturated fat); 5436kJ (1299 cal); 118.2g carbohydrate; 77.2g protein; 33.1g fibre; 925mg sodium
THURSDAY	green smoothie (page 34)	avocado and trout with fennel tzatziki sandwich (page 62)	asian beef rolls (page 44)	1 small pear	indian-spiced patties with carrot raita (page 70)	strawberry and pomegranate baked custard tarts (page 107)	47.3g total fat (5g saturated fat); 6379kJ (1524 cal); 189.4g carbohydrate; 63.6g protein; 30.8g fibre; 1253mg sodium
FRIDAY	breakfast quesadillas (page 18)	orange berry smoothie (page 35)	roast pumpkin and zucchini risoni salad (page 57)	½ cup straw-berries	kitchari (page 88)	baked apples and raspberries with quinoa almond crumble (page 108)	47.1g total fat (9.1g saturated fat); 6325kJ (1510 cal); 201.5g carbohydrate; 50.4g protein; 37.7g fibre; 797mg sodium
SATURDAY	strawberry and ricotta pancakes with honey (page 24)	1 small banana	hot and sour prawn and chicken soup (page 48)	1 small apple	five-spice beef with wasabi sauce (page 71)	chocolate semifreddo (page 100)	37.4g total fat (10g saturated fat); 5878kJ (1767 cal); 164.4g carbohydrate; 91.5g protein; 24.1g fibre; 1186mg sodium
SUNDAY	grilled eggs with spiced fennel and spinach (page 20)	1 small (100g) tub low-fat fruit yoghurt	moroccan lamb and chickpea wraps (page 43)	1 small nectarine	sticky chicken with noodles (page 64)	spelt crêpes with rhubarb in rose syrup (page 94)	52.4g total fat (12.3g saturated fat); 5302kJ (1166 cal); 145.7g carbohydrate; 101.7g protein; 29.4g fibre; 1438mg sodium

This menu planner is a guide only. It is important that you eat a balanced diet in order to get all the nutrients your body requires. See 'About the Recipes', page 10 for the recommended daily intakes.

BREAKFAST

strawberry and passionfruit breakfast trifle

PREP TIME 5 MINUTES SERVES 2

2 Weet-Bix (50g), broken into chunks

½ cup (40g) All-Bran cereal

⅓ cup (80ml) fresh passionfruit pulp

1 cup (280g) low-fat plain yoghurt

140g (1½ ounces) strawberries, sliced thinly

1 Layer half the Weet-Bix and All-Bran in two 1¼-cup (310ml) serving glasses. Top with half the passionfruit, yoghurt and strawberries.
2 Repeat with remaining Weet-Bix and All-Bran and yoghurt. Top with remaining strawberries and drizzle with remaining passionfruit.

tips Choose an elegant serving glass to make this easy pantry friendly breakfast into something special to start the day. Assemble the trifle when ready to eat so the cereals keep their crunch.

test kitchen tips

You will need about 4 passionfruit.
You can make the trifle with any
seasonal fruit combination or even
with canned fruit in natural juices.
Canned pears and frozen raspberries
work well together.

nutritional count per serving
▶ 2g total fat
▶ 0.5g saturated fat
▶ 722kJ (172 cal)
▶ 36.1g carbohydrate
▶ 16.2g protein
▶ 15.5g fibre
▶ 411mg sodium
▶ low GI

breakfast quesadillas

PREP + COOK TIME 20 MINUTES SERVES 2

125g (4 ounces) canned salt-reduced kidney beans, rinsed, drained, mashed

½ cup (85g) cooked brown rice

2 x 20cm (8-inch) wholemeal tortillas

⅓ cup (40g) grated extra-light tasty cheese

1 tablespoon olive oil

2 small eggs (100g)

TOMATO SALSA

160g (5 ounces) cherry tomatoes, chopped coarsely

2 tablespoons fresh coriander leaves (cilantro)

2 tablespoons fresh mint leaves

1 shallot (25g), chopped finely

2 teaspoons lemon juice

¼ teaspoon chilli flakes

1 Make tomato salsa.

2 Combine beans and rice in a medium bowl. Spoon the bean mixture over half of each tortilla and sprinkle with cheese. Fold over to enclose.

3 Heat half the oil in a large non-stick frying pan over medium heat; cook the quesadillas for 2 minutes each side or until brown and crisp. Set aside; cover to keep warm.

4 Heat remaining oil in same pan over low heat; cook eggs for 3 minutes or until cooked how you like them.

5 Top quesadillas with eggs and salsa.

TOMATO SALSA Combine ingredients in a medium bowl.

tips You could also poach the eggs. Microwave tortillas in the packet to separate them if they are sticking together. You can use microwave brown rice instead of cooking from raw, if you like. If you want to cook your own rice, cook ¼ cup of brown rice; use the ½ cup cooked rice required, and save the remainder for another use.

nutritional count per serving
▶ 17.7g total fat
▶ 4.9g saturated fat
▶ 1506kJ (359 cal)
▶ 29.6g carbohydrate
▶ 18.3g protein
▶ 6.4g fibre
▶ 355mg sodium
▶ medium GI

grilled eggs with spiced fennel and spinach

PREP + COOK TIME 20 MINUTES SERVES 2

2 teaspoons olive oil

1 clove garlic, crushed

1 fresh small red thai (serrano) chilli, sliced finely

½ small fennel bulb (100g), trimmed, sliced finely

100g (3 ounces) baby corn, halved

50g (1½ ounces) baby spinach leaves

2 eggs

1 tablespoon finely grated parmesan

2 slices rye sourdough bread (90g), toasted

1 Preheat grill (broiler) to high.

2 Heat oil in a large ovenproof non-stick frying pan over medium heat; cook garlic, chilli, fennel and corn, stirring occasionally, for 5 minutes or until fennel is soft. Add spinach; cook, stirring, for 1 minute or until spinach has wilted

3 Make two holes in the spinach mixture; break one egg into each hole. Sprinkle with parmesan.

4 Place under grill for 2 minutes or until eggs are cooked as desired.

5 Serve eggs and spinach mixture with toast.

tips Reserve fennel fronds to scatter over eggs as a garnish. You need an ovenproof frying pan as it goes under the grill, or you can cover the pan handle with a few layers of foil to protect it from the heat.

---

nutritional count per serving

▶ 18.3g total fat
▶ 21.6g protein
▶ 4.9g saturated fat
▶ 7.2g fibre
▶ 581kJ (378 cal)
▶ 404mg sodium
▶ 28g carbohydrate
▶ low GI

chia and almond toasted muesli

PREP + COOK TIME 20 MINUTES (+ COOLING) **SERVES** 2 (MAKES 1 CUP)

½ cup (45g) rolled oats

1 tablespoon chia seeds

2 tablespoons coarsely chopped almonds

¼ teaspoon mixed spice

2 teaspoons dark agave nectar

1 tablespoon sunflower seeds

1 tablespoon LSA

1 medium kiwi fruit (85g), sliced

50g (1½ ounces) strawberries, quartered

1 medium banana (200g), sliced

⅓ cup (95g) low-fat plain yoghurt

½ cup (125ml) skim milk

1 Preheat oven to 200°C/400°F.

2 Grease and line an oven tray with baking paper. Combine oats, chia, nuts and spice on tray. Drizzle with nectar; toss well. Bake for 10 minutes or until mixture is browned lightly. Cool on tray.

3 Transfer to a medium bowl; stir through seeds and LSA.

4 Divide evenly into two bowls. Top with fruit and yoghurt. Serve each with ¼ cup milk.

tip Make double or triple the muesli recipe and store it in an airtight container in the fridge for up to 3 months.

nutritional count per serving

▶ 16g total fat

▶ 1.5g saturated fat

▶ 1621kJ (387 cal)

▶ 40.5g carbohydrate

▶ 15.2g protein

▶ 9.6g fibre

▶ 78mg sodium

▶ low GI

test kitchen tips

If you are pressed for time, make one big omelette in a medium frying pan. You can change the filling depending on the seasonal vegetables available – try adding pumpkin or broccolini.

omelette with asparagus and mint

PREP + COOK TIME 20 MINUTES MAKES 2

1 baby new potato (40g), cut into 5mm (¼-inch) cubes

170g (5½ ounces) asparagus, trimmed

1 cup (120g) frozen peas

2 eggs

⅓ cup coarsely chopped fresh mint leaves

1 tablespoon olive oil

2 slices rye sourdough bread (90g), toasted

1 Cook potato in a small saucepan of boiling water for 3 minutes; add asparagus and peas, cook a further 1 minute or until asparagus is bright green and potato is tender; drain. When cool enough to handle, cut the asparagus in half; finely slice the stem ends crossways.

2 Lightly whisk eggs in a medium bowl; stir in potato, peas, mint and chopped asparagus ends.

3 Heat half the oil in a small non-stick frying pan on high; cook half the egg mixture, for about 2 minutes, pulling in the egg with a spatula to help it cook quickly. Fold over; slide onto a warm serving plate. Repeat with remaining oil and egg mixture to make second omelette.

4 Top omelettes with remaining asparagus and serve with toast.

nutritional count per serving
- ▶ 15.8g total fat
- ▶ 3.4g saturated fat
- ▶ 1400kJ (335 cal)
- ▶ 27.7g carbohydrate
- ▶ 16.3g protein
- ▶ 8.8g fibre
- ▶ 275mg sodium
- ▶ low GI

strawberry and ricotta pancakes with honey

PREP + COOK TIME 20 MINUTES SERVES 2

⅓ cup (80g) low-fat ricotta

2 eggs, separated

2 tablespoons caster (superfine) sugar

1 teaspoon vanilla extract

¼ cup (35g) buckwheat flour

⅓ cup (50g) wholemeal self-raising flour

¼ cup (45g) finely chopped strawberries

cooking-oil spray

150g (4½ ounces) strawberries, quartered

1 tablespoon coarsely chopped almonds

2 teaspoons honey

1 Whisk ricotta, egg yolks, sugar and extract in a small bowl. Stir in sifted flours and finely chopped strawberries.

2 Beat egg whites in a small bowl with an electric mixer until soft peaks form. Fold through ricotta mixture in two batches.

3 Spray a medium frying pan with oil; heat over medium heat. Spoon ¼ cup of batter into pan; cook pancakes for 3 minutes each side or until golden.

4 Serve pancakes with extra strawberries and nuts; drizzle with honey.

serving suggestion Dust each serve with ¼ teaspoon icing (confectioners') sugar.

nutritional count per serving
▶ 14.5g total fat
▶ 4.2g saturated fat
▶ 1812kJ (433 cal)
▶ 57.5g carbohydrate
▶ 16.2g protein
▶ 5.7g fibre
▶ 291mg sodium
▶ low GI

test kitchen tips

You can slightly spread the pancakes with the back of a spoon if the mixture doesn't spread when you add it to the pan. These pancakes are also great for dessert. You can make little pancakes, if you prefer, using just 1 tablespoon of mixture. Swap the strawberries for bananas, if you like.

fatteh

PREP + COOK TIME 15 MINUTES **SERVES** 2

This is a typical Lebanese breakfast dish. It's usually served on a big plate so friends, family, and even the neighbours, can share.

420g (12½ ounces) canned no-added-salt chickpeas (garbanzo beans), rinsed, drained

⅓ cup (80ml) water

1 wholemeal lebanese bread (80g)

3 teaspoons olive oil

1½ cups (420g) low-fat plain yoghurt

1 clove garlic, crushed

¼ cup (40g) pine nuts, toasted

¼ teaspoon sumac

1 Combine chickpeas and the water in a small saucepan over medium heat. Bring to the boil, reduce heat to low; simmer, covered, for 5 minutes. Using a potato masher, roughly mash chickpeas; keep warm.

2 Preheat grill (broiler) to medium. Brush bread with oil; place on an oven tray. Grill both sides until bread is dry and crisp (be careful not to burn the bread). Break bread into pieces.

3 Combine yoghurt and garlic in a small bowl.

4 To serve, divide bread pieces between two shallow plates; spoon over warm chickpea mash. Top with yoghurt mixture; scatter with pine nuts and sprinkle with sumac. Serve immediately.

tips If you find the chickpea mixture too thick add an extra teaspoon or two of hot water. You can easily double the recipe for a brunch with friends.
If you prefer, crisp the bread in a 200°C/400°F oven for about 5 minutes.

---

nutritional count per serving

▶ 25g total fat	▶ 27.1g protein
▶ 2.8g saturated fat	▶ 10.2g fibre
▶ 2350kJ (561 cal)	▶ 347mg sodium
▶ 50.9g carbohydrate	▶ low GI

breakfast muffins

PREP + COOK TIME 40 MINUTES MAKES 4

¼ cup (20g) rolled oats

¾ cup (120g) plain wholemeal flour

1 teaspoon ground cinnamon

½ teaspoon baking powder

¼ teaspoon bicarbonate of soda (baking soda)

2 tablespoons sultanas

1 egg, beaten lightly

¼ cup (60ml) buttermilk

¼ cup (55g) apple puree

¼ cup (75g) mashed banana

1 teaspoon vanilla extract

1 teaspoon honey, warmed

1 Preheat oven to 200°C/400°F. Line four holes of a 6-hole (¾-cup/180ml) texas muffin pan with baking paper squares or muffin cases.
2 Reserve 2 teaspoons of the oats. Sift flour, cinnamon, baking powder and soda in a medium bowl. Add sultanas and the remaining oats to the flour mixture; stir in combined egg, buttermilk, puree, banana and extract.
3 Divide mixture among prepared pan holes; sprinkle with reserved oats. Bake for 20 minutes.
4 Brush tops with honey. Bake a further 5 minutes or until golden and cooked when tested with a skewer. Stand muffins in pan for 5 minutes before turning, top-side up, onto a wire rack to cool.

tips You need 1 small ripe banana (130g), to get the amount of mashed banana needed for these muffins. Muffins are suitable to freeze, stored in an airtight container, for up to 3 months. The muffins are best eaten warm; reheat, one at a time, in a microwave oven for about 20 seconds on HIGH (100%).

nutritional count per muffin

▶ 2.8g total fat	▶ 7.1g protein
▶ 0.8g saturated fat	▶ 5.3g fibre
▶ 877kJ (209 cal)	▶ 375mg sodium
▶ 36.5g carbohydrate	▶ medium GI

soy porridge with banana, whole seeds and almonds

PREP + COOK TIME 10 MINUTES SERVES 2

1 cup (90g) rolled oats

1½ cups (375ml) reduced-fat soy milk

¼ teaspoon ground cinnamon

1 tablespoon coarsely chopped dry-roasted almonds

¼ teaspoon each poppy seeds, sesame seeds, black chia seeds and linseeds

2 teaspoons sunflower seeds

½ medium banana (165g), sliced thickly

2 teaspoons pure maple syrup

1 Place oats, soy milk and cinnamon in a small saucepan over low heat, bring to a gentle simmer; cook, stirring occasionally, for 5 minutes or until mixture has thickened and oats are tender.

2 Meanwhile, combine nuts and seeds in a small bowl.

3 Serve porridge topped with banana; sprinkle with nut and seed mixture, drizzle with maple syrup.

tip Use traditional rolled oats rather than instant oats for a better texture. You can use white chia seeds, if you like. Swap banana for a low-GI fruit such as strawberries, grapes, peaches or plums.

nutritional count per serving
▶ 9.2g total fat
▶ 1.1g saturated fat
▶ 1487kJ (355 cal)
▶ 51.4g carbohydrate
▶ 9.2g protein
▶ 6.7g fibre
▶ 89mg sodium
▶ low GI

quinoa porridge

PREP + COOK TIME 20 MINUTES SERVES 2

½ cup (100g) white quinoa, rinsed, drained

1½ cups (375ml) water

½ cup (125ml) skim milk

1 medium apple (150g), grated coarsely

100g (3 ounces) red seedless grapes, halved

2 tablespoons pistachios, toasted, chopped coarsely

1 tablespoon honey

1 Combine quinoa and the water in a small saucepan; bring to the boil. Reduce heat; simmer, covered, for 10 minutes. Add milk; cook, covered, a further 5 minutes or until quinoa is tender.
2 Stir in apple and half the grapes.
3 Serve porridge, topped with remaining grapes, nuts and drizzled with honey.

tips We used a pink lady apple in this recipe. Most quinoa comes rinsed, but it's a good habit to rinse it yourself under cold water until the water runs clear, then drain it. This removes any remaining outer coating, which has a bitter taste. Quinoa absorbs a lot of liquid. Depending how you like your porridge, add a little boiling water at the end of step 1 to thin it out.

nutritional count per serving
- ▶ 8.9g total fat
- ▶ 1g saturated fat
- ▶ 1642kJ (392 cal)
- ▶ 63g carbohydrate
- ▶ 12.2g protein
- ▶ 5.6g fibre
- ▶ 53mg sodium
- ▶ low GI

zucchini and corn frittatas

PREP + COOK TIME 40 MINUTES **SERVES** 2

3 teaspoons semolina

2 small zucchini (180g)

1 baby new potato (40g), unpeeled

2 eggs

⅓ cup (80g) low-fat ricotta

1 tablespoon creamed corn

1 tablespoon finely chopped fresh flat-leaf parsley

150g (4½ ounces) truss cherry tomatoes

2 teaspoons olive oil

2 slices soy linseed sourdough bread (90g), toasted

1 Preheat oven to 220°C/425°F. Lightly grease two holes of a 6-hole (¾-cup/180ml) texas muffin pan. Sprinkle greased holes with semolina.

2 Using a vegetable peeler; cut one zucchini into ribbons. Line pan holes with zucchini, overlapping at slightly different angles. Coarsely grate remaining zucchini and potato, squeezing out excess liquid.

3 Whisk eggs, ricotta, corn, parsley, grated zucchini and potato in a small bowl. Spoon into prepared holes. Bake for 25 minutes.

4 Place tomatoes on an oven tray; drizzle with oil. Bake for 10 minutes with frittatas until tomatoes soften and frittatas are golden and set.

5 Serve frittatas and tomatoes; accompany with toast.

tip These frittatas are great to pack for a work lunch as they can be eaten warm or cold. Make them a day ahead and reheat in a microwave oven on MEDIUM (50%) for about 2 minutes or until heated through.

nutritional count per serving

- ▶ 15.8g total fat
- ▶ 4.3g saturated fat
- ▶ 1450kJ (346 cal)
- ▶ 27g carbohydrate
- ▶ 20.8g protein
- ▶ 7g fibre
- ▶ 440mg sodium
- ▶ low GI

toast with avocado, tahini and sumac tomatoes

PREP + COOK TIME 40 MINUTES **SERVES** 2

3 medium roma (egg) tomatoes (225g), halved lengthways

½ teaspoon sumac

cooking-oil spray

½ clove garlic, crushed

¼ cup (70g) low-fat plain yoghurt

1 tablespoon tahini (sesame seed paste)

1 teaspoon lemon juice

½ small avocado (100g)

2 slices wholegrain sourdough bread (120g), toasted

1 Preheat oven to 180°C/350°F.

2 Grease and line a small oven tray with baking paper. Place tomato on tray, skin-side down; sprinkle sumac over cut surfaces, spray lightly with olive oil. Roast for 30 minutes or until tomato has collapsed slightly.

3 Place garlic, yoghurt, tahini and juice in a small bowl; whisk to combine.

4 Spread half the avocado thickly over each toast slice. Spoon tahini mixture over avocado and top with tomatoes.

tips We cut the sourdough into 1.5cm (¾-inch) slices. Cook extra sumac tomatoes and keep them in the fridge to have on hand and use as a delicious ingredient in pasta, salads and sandwiches. Store them in an airtight container for up to a week.

nutritional count per serving
▶ 17.4g total fat
▶ 3g saturated fat
▶ 1490kJ (356 cal)
▶ 33.5g carbohydrate
▶ 12.2g protein
▶ 7.2g fibre
▶ 371mg sodium
▶ low GI

green smoothie

PREP TIME 10 MINUTES **SERVES** 2

1 Roughly chop 1 medium banana and 2 kiwi fruit.
2 Blend or process fruit with 30g (1 ounce) baby spinach leaves, 1 cup almond milk, 1 tablespoon honey and 2 teaspoons chia seeds until smooth.

tip Chia seeds are available from supermarkets and health food stores. They come in black or white varieties and either type would work in this recipe. You could omit chia seeds if you like.

pb & j smoothie

PREP TIME 5 MINUTES **SERVES** 2

1 Blend or process 1½ cups frozen strawberries, 1½ tablespoons smooth light peanut butter, 2 tablespoons wheat germ, 1 tablespoon brown rice malt syrup and 1½ cups low-fat milk until smooth.

tip You could also use honey or agave syrup instead of the brown rice malt syrup.

nutritional count per serving
▶ 15.6g total fat	▶ 7.3g protein
▶ 1g saturated fat	▶ 7.1g fibre
▶ 1297kJ (310 cal)	▶ 12mg sodium
▶ 32.6g carbohydrate	▶ low GI

nutritional count per serving
▶ 10.3g total fat	▶ 15.8g protein
▶ 1.8g saturated fat	▶ 5.9g fibre
▶ 1260kJ (301 cal)	▶ 234mg sodium
▶ 33.7g carbohydrate	▶ low GI

orange berry smoothie

PREP TIME 10 MINUTES **SERVES** 2

1 Roughly chop 1 medium peeled orange and 1 medium cored pear.
2 Blend or process fruit with 1 cup frozen mixed berries, 150g (4½ ounces) low-fat, low-sugar vanilla yoghurt and ¼ cup pomegranate juice until smooth.

tip You could use apple juice instead of the pomegranate juice, if you prefer.

invigorating fruit and vegetable juice

PREP TIME 10 MINUTES **SERVES** 2 (MAKES 750ML)

1 Push 2 coarsely chopped large beetroot, 2 trimmed celery stalks, 130g (4 ounces) silver beet leaves (swiss chard), 2 chopped large green apples, 1 cup fresh flat-leaf parsley, 1 segmented medium lemon and 20g (¾-ounce) peeled fresh ginger through a juice extractor into a jug. Stir; serve immediately.

tip Have the fruit washed and chopped, and on hand in the refrigerator to save time; juice just before serving to retain the nutrients in the fruit and vegetables.

nutritional count per serving
- 0.4g total fat
- 6.4g protein
- 0.1g saturated fat
- 9.4g fibre
- 862kJ (206 cal)
- 62mg sodium
- 38.9g carbohydrate
- low GI

nutritional count per serving
- 0.8g total fat
- 7.3g protein
- 0g saturated fat
- 2.4g fibre
- 917kJ (219 cal)
- 370mg sodium
- 37.8g carbohydrate
- low GI

LUNCH

asian-style chicken salad

PREP + COOK TIME 15 MINUTES SERVES 2

100g (3 ounces) soba noodles

1½ cups (240g) shredded cooked skinless chicken breast

6 iceberg lettuce leaves, torn

1 lebanese cucumber (130g), sliced thinly

½ small red onion (50g), sliced thinly

1 large mandarin (250g), segmented

1 small avocado (200g), chopped coarsely

2 teaspoons sesame seeds, toasted

ASIAN DRESSING

2 tablespoons rice wine vinegar

1 tablespoon fresh mandarin juice

2 teaspoons salt-reduced soy sauce

1 teaspoon grated fresh ginger

½ teaspoon sesame oil

1 Make asian dressing.
2 Cook noodles in a large saucepan of boiling water until tender; drain. Rinse under cold water; drain.
3 Combine all ingredients in a large bowl. Drizzle with dressing.

ASIAN DRESSING Combine ingredients in a small bowl.

tips You can use store-bought barbecue chicken, leftover roast chicken, or just bake or poach two small chicken breasts. Swap the soba noodles for rice or egg noodles.

nutritional count per serving
▶ 24.2g total fat
▶ 5.3g saturated fat
▶ 2509kJ (599 cal)
▶ 40.5g carbohydrate
▶ 47.1g protein
▶ 12.3g fibre
▶ 266mg sodium
▶ low GI

quinoa salad with char-grilled vegetables and tuna

PREP + COOK TIME 25 MINUTES **SERVES** 2

1 small red capsicum (bell pepper) (150g), quartered

1 medium zucchini (120g), sliced thinly

1 baby eggplant (60g), sliced thinly

1 small red onion (100g), cut into wedges

⅓ cup (70g) quinoa, rinsed, drained

⅔ cup (160ml) water

2 teaspoons olive oil

¼ cup (60ml) lemon juice

1 teaspoon dijon mustard

185g (6½ ounces) canned tuna in springwater, drained

2 tablespoons baby basil leaves

1 Cook capsicum, zucchini, eggplant and onion on a heated oiled grill plate (or grill or barbecue) until tender. Slice capsicum thickly.

2 Meanwhile, place quinoa in a small saucepan with the water; bring to the boil. Reduce heat to low; simmer, covered, for 15 minutes or until tender and water is absorbed. Remove from heat; stand for 10 minutes, then fluff with a fork.

3 Combine oil, juice and mustard in a screw-top jar; shake well.

4 Place quinoa, vegetables and tuna in a bowl with dressing; toss gently to combine. Serve topped with basil leaves.

tips Vegetables can be grilled a day ahead; store, covered, in the fridge. The salad can be served warm or cold; add some rocket (arugula) or spinach leaves, if you like.

nutritional count per serving
▶ 9.1g total fat
▶ 1.7g saturated fat
▶ 1332kJ (318 cal)
▶ 28.9g carbohydrate
▶ 26g protein
▶ 5.8g fibre
▶ 118g sodium
▶ low GI

spiced lentil and roasted kumara soup

PREP + COOK TIME 45 MINUTES SERVES 2

1 small kumara (orange sweet potato) (250g), cut into 2cm (¾-inch) cubes

cooking-oil spray

1 small brown onion (80g), chopped coarsely

1 clove garlic, crushed

½ cup (125ml) salt-reduced vegetable stock

½ teaspoon each ground cumin and coriander

¼ teaspoon turmeric

¼ cup (50g) dried red lentils, rinsed, drained

2 cups (500ml) water

⅓ cup (95g) low-fat plain yoghurt

2 tablespoons finely chopped fresh coriander (cilantro)

1 Preheat oven to 220°C/425°F. Place kumara on a baking-paper-lined oven tray; spray with oil. Bake for 25 minutes until golden and tender.

2 Meanwhile, cook onion, garlic and 2 tablespoons of the stock in a medium saucepan over high heat, stirring, for 3 minutes or until onion is tender. Add spices; cook, stirring, for 30 seconds or until fragrant. Stir in lentils, remaining stock and the water; bring to the boil. Reduce heat; simmer, uncovered, for 15 minutes or until lentils are tender. Add kumara. Cook for 5 minutes. Cool mixture 10 minutes.

3 Blend or process mixture until smooth. Return mixture to pan; stir until hot.

4 Combine yoghurt and coriander in a small bowl. Serve soup topped with yoghurt mixture and extra coriander leaves, if you like.

nutritional count per serving
- ▶ 2.7g total fat
- ▶ 0.5g saturated fat
- ▶ 877kJ (209 cal)
- ▶ 30.9g carbohydrate
- ▶ 12g protein
- ▶ 6.7g fibre
- ▶ 296mg sodium
- ▶ low GI

test kitchen tips

Soup can be made a day ahead; store, covered, in the fridge. Freeze the soup without the yoghurt mixture in an airtight container for up to 3 months. Defrost in the fridge overnight and reheat in a small saucepan on the stove over medium heat for about 10 minutes or until hot.

moroccan lamb and chickpea wraps

PREP + COOK TIME 15 MINUTES **SERVES** 2

200g (6 ounces) lamb fillets

125g (4 ounces) canned chickpeas (garbanzo beans), rinsed, drained

60g (2 ounces) drained char-grilled capsicum (bell pepper), sliced thinly

½ small red onion (50g), chopped finely

1 large tomato, chopped finely

¼ cup loosely packed fresh mint leaves

2 tablespoons lemon juice

1 teaspoon olive oil

¼ cup (70g) low-fat plain yoghurt

¼ teaspoon harissa paste

6 butter (boston) lettuce leaves

2 rye mountain breads (50g)

1 Cook lamb on a heated oiled grill plate (or grill or barbecue) until cooked as desired. Cover lamb; rest for 5 minutes, then slice thickly.

2 Meanwhile, combine chickpeas, capsicum, onion, tomato, mint, juice and oil in a bowl; stir to combine.

3 Combine yoghurt and harissa in a small bowl.

4 Divide yoghurt mixture, lettuce, lamb and chickpea mixture between wraps. Roll firmly to enclose filling.

tips There are many types of mountain bread available; choose your favourite for this recipe. Harissa is a very hot paste; there are many different brands of harissa paste available, and the strengths vary enormously. Reduce the amount of harissa to suit your taste if you are not used to the fiery heat.

nutritional count per serving
- 9.9g total fat
- 2.6g saturated fat
- 1593kJ (381 cal)
- 34.8g carbohydrate
- 33.3g protein
- 5.9g fibre
- 389mg sodium
- low GI

asian beef rolls

PREP TIME 15 MINUTES **SERVES** 2

1 tablespoon smooth salt-reduced peanut butter

1 teaspoon salt-reduced soy sauce

1 tablespoon boiling water

2 long wholegrain bread rolls (100g), split

60g (2 ounces) thinly sliced salt-reduced rare roast beef

4 butter (boston) lettuce leaves

1 small carrot (70g), sliced thinly

4 long sprigs fresh coriander leaves (cilantro)

1 green onion (scallion), halved crossways

½ fresh long red chilli, sliced thinly

1 Combine peanut butter, sauce and the water in a small bowl. Spread over the inside of bread rolls.

2 Sandwich beef, lettuce, carrot, coriander, green onion and chilli between rolls. Serve with a squeeze of lime, if you like.

tip You could use left-over roast beef or char-grill a rump steak.

---

nutritional count per serving
- ▶ 9.8g total fat
- ▶ 1.9g saturated fat
- ▶ 1166kJ (279 cal)
- ▶ 27.6g carbohydrate
- ▶ 16.8g protein
- ▶ 5.7g fibre
- ▶ 403mg sodium
- ▶ medium GI

tomato and fennel soup

PREP + COOK TIME 50 MINUTES SERVES 2

1 large fennel bulb (550g)

1 small kumara (orange sweet potato) (250g), cut into 2cm (¾-inch) pieces

4 small tomatoes (360g), halved

1 medium red onion (170g), cut into wedges

2 cloves garlic, unpeeled

cooking-oil spray

2½ cups (625ml) homemade vegetable stock (see inner back flap)

⅓ cup (55g) natural almonds, chopped coarsely

1 Preheat oven to 200°C/400°F. Line a large oven tray with baking paper.

2 Trim fennel, reserving 1 tablespoon of fennel fronds; cut fennel into wedges. Combine fennel, kumara, tomato, onion and garlic on tray. Lightly spray with oil. Roast 30 minutes or until tender and browned.

3 Peel garlic; blend or process kumara, tomatoes, fennel, onion, garlic and stock until smooth.

4 Place the soup in a medium saucepan. Bring to the boil. Serve soup sprinkled with nuts and reserved fennel fronds.

tip Make the soup ahead of time and freeze for up to 3 months or refrigerate for 1 week. You can use packaged reduced-salt vegetable stock instead of homemade stock, if you like.

nutritional count per serving
- 17.5g total fat
- 1.3g saturated fat
- 1756kJ (419 cal)
- 38.8g carbohydrate
- 14.7g protein
- 12.5g fibre
- 148mg sodium
- low GI

test kitchen tips

This recipe is perfect for any lunchbox as you can make it the night before; store, covered, in the fridge. If you're short of time, try making this salad with quinoa instead of rice; it will take less than half the time to cook and has a great fibre content, just like brown rice. You could use chicken breast or lamb fillets instead of the turkey.

turkey and brown rice salad

PREP + COOK TIME 40 MINUTES SERVES 2

⅔ cup (130g) brown rice

100g (3 ounces) green beans, trimmed, halved lengthways

200g (6½ ounces) turkey breast steaks

3 red radishes (105g), sliced thinly

1 lebanese cucumber (130g), halved, sliced thinly

40g (1½ ounces) goat's cheese, crumbled

2 green onions (scallions), sliced thinly

1 trimmed celery stalk (100g), sliced thinly

1 tablespoon cashews, toasted, coarsely chopped

50g (1½ ounces) baby rocket leaves (arugula)

¼ cup loosely packed torn fresh basil leaves

1 tablespoon olive oil

2 tablespoons lemon juice

1 Place rice in a medium saucepan, cover with water; bring to the boil. Reduce heat; simmer, uncovered, for 35 minutes or until tender. Drain; rinse under cold water. Drain well.

2 Meanwhile, cook beans in a small saucepan of boiling water for 3 minutes or until just tender. Drain; refresh under cold water, drain.

3 Cook turkey on a heated oiled grill pan (or grill or barbecue) for 3 minutes each side or until cooked through. Cover; rest for 5 minutes, then slice thickly.

4 Combine rice with beans, turkey, radish, cucumber, cheese, onion, celery, nuts, rocket and basil in a large bowl. Drizzle with combined oil and juice; toss to combine.

nutritional count per serving
- 21.6g total fat
- 5.9g saturated fat
- 2422kJ (579 cal)
- 57.4g carbohydrate
- 34.3g protein
- 6.9g fibre
- 400mg sodium
- high GI

hot and sour prawn and chicken soup

PREP + COOK TIME 30 MINUTES **SERVES** 2

3 cups (750ml) water

4 fresh kaffir lime leaves, torn

40g (¾ ounce) fresh ginger, sliced thickly

1 fresh small red thai (serrano) chilli, sliced thinly

100g (3 ounces) dried rice noodles

4 green king prawns (shrimp) (140g)

100g (3 ounces) chicken breast, sliced thinly

1 tablespoon lime juice

100g (3 ounces) snow peas, shredded

350g (8 ounces) baby choy sum, trimmed, chopped coarsely

½ cup (40g) bean sprouts

¼ cup each loosely packed fresh coriander (cilantro), mint and thai basil leaves

1 Combine the water, lime leaves, ginger and half the chilli in a medium saucepan over high heat; bring to the boil. Reduce heat; simmer, covered, for 10 minutes; discard leaves and ginger.

2 Meanwhile, cook noodles in a medium saucepan of boiling water according to packet directions; drain.

3 Shell and devein prawns leaving tails intact. Add prawns and chicken to broth; simmer for 3 minutes or until chicken and prawns are cooked. Stir in lime juice.

4 Divide noodles, snow peas and choy sum between two serving bowls; ladle over broth mixture. Top with sprouts, herbs and remaining chilli.

tip Make sure the broth is piping hot so it will slightly cook the choy sum and snow peas. If you can't find baby choy sum, use ½ bunch of normal choy sum or another asian green. Kaffir lime leaves are sold in small packets. Freeze the remaining leaves – they lose a bit of colour but keep all their flavour. You can use a packaged salt-reduced chicken stock instead of the water, if you like.

nutritional count per serving
▶ 3.8g total fat
▶ 0.9g saturated fat
▶ 1101kJ (263 cal)
▶ 28.4g carbohydrate
▶ 25g protein
▶ 5.8g fibre
▶ 449mg sodium
▶ medium GI

vegetable rösti with smoked salmon and sour cream

PREP + COOK TIME 30 MINUTES **SERVES** 2

½ small kumara (orange sweet potato) (125g), peeled, grated coarsely

2 shallots (50g), sliced finely

1 medium silver beet leaf (swiss chard) (65g), trimmed, shredded

1 small zucchini (90g), grated coarsely

1 egg, beaten lightly

⅓ cup (50g) wholemeal spelt flour

1 tablespoon olive oil

120g (4 ounces) smoked trout

1½ tablespoons light sour cream

1 tablespoon fresh dill sprigs

1 Combine kumara, shallot, silver beet, zucchini, egg and flour in a large bowl; mix well. Divide mixture into four equal portions.

2 Heat oil in a large non-stick frying pan over medium heat, place kumara mixture into pan; press each portion down with spatula to flatten. Cook 4 minutes each side or until rösti are golden and cooked through.

3 Serve rösti topped with smoked trout, sour cream and dill.

tip Cooked rösti can be stored in the refrigerator overnight and reheated in a sandwich press.

nutritional count per serving

▶ 16.5g total fat	▶ 21.8g protein
▶ 4.6g saturated fat	▶ 5g fibre
▶ 1466kJ (350 cal)	▶ 430mg sodium
▶ 27g carbohydrate	▶ low GI

nutritional count per serving

▶ 23.6g total fat	▶ 16.2g protein
▶ 3.6g saturated fat	▶ 18.1g fibre
▶ 2271kJ (543 cal)	▶ 440mg sodium
▶ 56.5g carbohydrate	▶ low GI

wholemeal pasta with cauliflower and olives

PREP + COOK TIME 30 MINUTES **SERVES** 2

2 tablespoons olive oil

2 cloves garlic, crushed

1 fresh small red thai chilli (serrano), chopped finely

½ small cauliflower (500g), trimmed, cut into florets

400g (12½ ounces) canned no-added-salt diced tomatoes

½ cup (125ml) water

150g (4½ ounces) wholemeal penne

2 tablespoons pitted black olives, halved

2 tablespoons finely chopped fresh flat-leaf parsley

1 tablespoon fresh baby basil leaves

1 Heat oil in a large saucepan over low heat, add garlic and chilli; cook, stirring, for 2 minutes or until soft.
2 Add cauliflower, tomato and the water to pan; increase heat to medium. Simmer, covered, for 20 minutes or until cauliflower is tender.
3 Meanwhile, cook pasta in a large saucepan of boiling water until just tender; drain. Add pasta to sauce with olives, parsley and basil; toss to combine.

tip The sauce can be made a day ahead; store, covered, in the fridge. Reheat in a microwave oven on MEDIUM-HIGH (75%) for 5 minutes or until hot, or in a large saucepan over medium heat until hot.

pork and veal lasagne with spinach

PREP + COOK TIME 1½ HOURS **SERVES** 2

1 tablespoon olive oil

200g (6½ ounces) mushrooms, chopped coarsely

1 medium brown onion (150g), chopped finely

1 clove garlic, crushed

200g (6½ ounces) lean minced (ground) pork and veal mixture (see tips)

400g (12½ ounces) canned no-added-salt diced tomatoes

1 tablespoon finely chopped fresh oregano

1 cup (250ml) skim milk

1¼ tablespoons cornflour (cornstarch)

250g (8 ounces) frozen chopped spinach, thawed

1 fresh lasagne sheet (50g), cut into thirds

¼ cup (25g) grated mozzarella

1 Preheat oven to 200°C/400°F. Lightly grease a 1-litre (4-cup) ovenproof dish.

2 Heat half the oil in a medium frying pan over high heat; cook mushrooms, stirring, for 5 minutes or until browned. Remove from pan.

3 Heat remaining oil in same pan over medium heat; cook onion and garlic, stirring, for 3 minutes or until onion is softened.

4 Increase heat to high, add mince to pan; cook, stirring, for 3 minutes or until browned. Return mushrooms to pan with tomatoes and oregano; simmer, covered, over low heat, for 10 minutes, stirring occasionally.

5 Meanwhile, combine milk and cornflour in a small saucepan; whisk until smooth. Cook, stirring, over medium heat, for 5 minutes or until mixture boils and thickens. Remove from heat.

6 Squeeze excess moisture from spinach.

7 Spoon a third of the mince mixture into prepared dish. Cover with one lasagne sheet. Spoon over another third of the mince mixture; top with spinach and another lasagne sheet. Spoon over remaining mince mixture; cover with lasagne sheet. Spoon over white sauce; sprinkle with cheese.

8 Place dish on an oven tray; bake for 45 minutes or until lasagne is tender and cheese is golden. Sprinkle with extra oregano leaves, if you like.

serving suggestion Serve with a leafy green salad.

tips You could make this lasagne with wholemeal pasta sheets for extra fibre. This lasagne will freeze well so make a double or triple batch in a larger ovenproof dish and freeze (once cooled) in individual airtight containers for up to 1 month. You could replace the oregano with basil. Add a little freshly grated nutmeg to the white sauce, if you like. We used cup mushrooms here, but use your favourite type.
Some butcher's sell a pork and veal mixture, which is what we've used here. If it is not available, buy half the amount in pork mince and half the amount in veal mince.

nutritional count per serving
▶ 18.9g total fat
▶ 5.4g saturated fat
▶ 1927kJ (460 cal)
▶ 28.3g carbohydrate
▶ 41.5g protein
▶ 13.4g fibre
▶ 445mg sodium
▶ low GI

nutritional count per serving

▶ 11.1g total fat
▶ 2.7g saturated fat
▶ 1199kJ (286 cal)
▶ 27.7g carbohydrate
▶ 15.7g protein
▶ 6.1g fibre
▶ 446mg sodium
▶ medium GI

spinach and cheese snails

PREP + COOK TIME 50 MINUTES SERVES 2

6 medium silver beet leaves (swiss chard) (195g), trimmed, chopped roughly

cooking-oil spray

4 green onions (scallions), sliced thinly

1 clove garlic, crushed

½ cup (100g) low-fat low-salt cottage cheese

¼ cup finely chopped fresh dill leaves

¼ cup finely chopped fresh flat-leaf parsley

1 egg yolk

4 sheets fillo pastry

TOMATO SALAD

2 medium roma (egg) tomatoes (150g), cut into wedges

1 small red onion (100g), sliced thinly

1 teaspoon olive oil

1 tablespoon fresh oregano leaves

1 Preheat oven to 180°C/350°F. Grease and line an oven tray with baking paper.
2 Cook silver beet in a large saucepan of boiling water for 5 minutes; drain, rinse under cold running water. Squeeze out excess moisture, place silver beet in a large bowl.
3 Spray a medium frying pan with oil; heat over low heat. Add onion and garlic to pan; cook, stirring occasionally, for 3 minutes or until soft.
4 Add onion mixture to silver beet with cheese, herbs and egg yolk; stir until well combined.
5 Spray one sheet of pastry with oil, top with another sheet. Spoon half the silver beet mixture along one long edge of the pastry and roll up tightly to form a sausage shape. Roll pastry to make a snail shape. Place on oven tray. Repeat with remaining pastry and silver beet mixture.
6 Spray each snail lightly with oil; bake for 35 minutes or until pastry is crisp and golden.
7 Meanwhile, make tomato salad. Serve snails with salad.

TOMATO SALAD Combine ingredients in a medium bowl.

tip Make the filling for the snail a day ahead. The recipe is best baked just before serving.

italian white bean and cabbage soup

PREP + COOK TIME 30 MINUTES (+ REFRIGERATION & STANDING) SERVES 2

You need to make the stock a day ahead.

1.5 litres (6 cups) homemade vegetable stock (see back inner flap) (see tips)

1 cup (200g) dried cannellini beans

1 teaspoon olive oil

1 medium brown onion (150g), chopped coarsely

1 celery stalk (150g), chopped coarsely

2 cloves garlic, sliced thinly

1 slice prosciutto (15g)

300g (9½ ounces) cabbage, shredded finely

3 teaspoons lemon juice

2 tablespoons fresh flat-leaf parsley leaves

1 Make vegetable stock.
2 Place beans in a medium bowl, cover with water; stand overnight. Rinse under cold water; drain.
3 Heat oil in a large saucepan over medium heat; cook onion, celery and garlic, stirring, for 5 minutes or until softened. Add stock and beans to the pan, bring to the boil; reduce heat, simmer, covered, for 50 minutes or until beans are tender.
4 Cook prosciutto in a non-stick frying pan, over high heat, for 1 minute each side or until crisp; break into shards.
5 Add cabbage to soup; simmer, covered, for 5 minutes or until just wilted. Stir in juice. Serve soup topped with prosciutto and parsley leaves.

tips Soak a large quantity of beans and boil until tender, store in the freezer in airtight bags, so that you have beans on hand. You can use thinly sliced bacon or leftover roasted chicken instead of prosciutto. Add some finely shredded fresh sage leaves when frying the onion, if you like. You can use packaged low-fat, no-salt vegtable stock instead of homemade stock, if you like.

nutritional count per serving

▶ 24g total fat
▶ 3.7g saturated fat
▶ 2199kJ (525 cal)
▶ 28.4g carbohydrate
▶ 38.8g protein
▶ 29.8g fibre
▶ 338mg sodium
▶ low GI

roast pumpkin and zucchini risoni salad

PREP + COOK TIME 45 MINUTES **SERVES** 2

250g (8 ounces) jap pumpkin, chopped coarsely

1 large zucchini (150g), chopped coarsely

1 small red onion (100g), cut into wedges

1 stalk fresh rosemary

9 small garlic cloves (35g), unpeeled

cooking-oil spray

⅓ cup (75g) risoni pasta

¼ cup (70g) low-fat plain yoghurt

1 tablespoon balsamic vinegar

1 cup loosely packed fresh basil leaves, torn

20g (¾ ounce) baby spinach leaves

1 tablespoon currants

2 tablespoons pine nuts, toasted

1 Preheat oven to 220°C/425°F.

2 Line a large roasting tray with baking paper. Combine pumpkin, zucchini, onion, rosemary and unpeeled garlic on the tray. Lightly spray with oil. Roast for 30 minutes or until tender and browned. Discard rosemary stalk.

3 Meanwhile, cook risoni in a large saucepan of boiling water until pasta is just tender. Drain, rinse under cold water, drain.

4 Peel garlic, place in a small bowl; mash with a fork. Add yoghurt and vinegar; stir to combine.

5 Combine the roasted vegetables in a large dish with risoni, basil, spinach, currants and pine nuts; stir through yoghurt mixture until just combined.

tips You can make this salad with other small pasta such as macaroni. Make the salad a day ahead but only dress it just before serving.

nutritional count per serving
▶ 13.3g total fat
▶ 12.4g protein
▶ 1.1g saturated fat
▶ 9.8g fibre
▶ 1570kJ (375 cal)
▶ 42mg sodium
▶ 46.1g carbohydrate
▶ medium GI

chermoula tuna, chickpea and broad bean salad

PREP + COOK TIME 30 MINUTES (+ REFRIGERATION) **SERVES** 2

200g (6½-ounce) piece tuna steak

1 cup (150g) frozen broad (fava) beans

150g (4½ ounces) green beans, trimmed, cut into thirds

420g (13½ ounce) canned no-added salt chickpeas (garbanzo beans), rinsed, drained

½ cup firmly packed fresh flat-leaf parsley leaves

1 medium lemon (140g), peeled, segmented

1 tablespoon lemon juice

1 tablespoon olive oil

CHERMOULA

½ small red onion (50g), chopped coarsely

1 clove garlic, peeled

1 cup firmly packed fresh coriander (cilantro), chopped roughly

1 cup firmly packed fresh flat-leaf parsley, chopped coarsely

1 teaspoon each ground cumin and smoked paprika

1 tablespoon olive oil

1 Make chermoula. Reserve three-quarters of the chermoula.

2 Place tuna in a shallow dish with remaining chermoula; toss to coat. Cover, refrigerate for 30 minutes.

3 Meanwhile, place broad beans in a heatproof bowl, cover with boiling water; stand for 2 minutes. Rinse under cold water; drain. Peel beans.

4 Boil, steam or microwave green beans until just tender; drain, rinse under cold water, drain.

5 Cook tuna on a heated oiled grill plate (or grill or barbecue) for 2 minutes each side or until slightly charred on the outside but still rare in the centre; cover, stand for 5 minutes. Cut tuna, across the grain, into slices.

6 Combine broad beans, green beans, chickpeas, parsley and lemon segments in a medium bowl with combined juice and oil. Serve tuna with salad and top with reserved chermoula.

CHERMOULA Blend or process ingredients until just combined.

tips Swap the tuna for salmon in this recipe. Purchase sashimi grade tuna for this recipe. If the chermoula ingredients aren't blending well, add 1 tablespoon water to the mixture.

nutritional count per serving
▶ 23.6g total fat
▶ 3.7g saturated fat
▶ 2208kJ (527 cal)
▶ 29.6g carbohydrate
▶ 43.7g protein
▶ 18.1g fibre
▶ 220mg sodium
▶ medium GI

vietnamese pancakes with prawns

PREP + COOK TIME 30 MINUTES **SERVES** 4

8 cooked tiger prawns (shrimp) (280g)

½ cup (90g) rice flour

¼ teaspoon turmeric

2 tablespoons reduced-fat coconut milk

⅔ cup (160ml) water

1 egg

1 tablespoon olive oil

8 butter (boston) lettuce leaves (pulled from the centre of the lettuce)

1 lebanese cucumber (130g), sliced thinly

1 medium carrot (120g), sliced into ribbons

1 cup (80g) bean sprouts

½ bunch fresh mint leaves

½ bunch fresh thai basil leaves

CHILLI DIPPING SAUCE

1 tablespoon warm water

1 tablespoon lemon juice

2 teaspoons low-GI cane sugar

½ teaspoon fish sauce

½ clove garlic, crushed

1 fresh small red thai chilli (serrano), chopped finely

1 Make chilli dipping sauce.

2 Shell and devein prawns leaving tails intact.

3 Place rice flour and turmeric in a medium bowl. Add coconut milk, the water and egg; whisk until well combined and batter is smooth.

4 Heat 1 teaspoon of the oil in a large non-stick frying pan (base measurement 23cm/9-inches) over medium heat; pour a quarter of the batter into pan, swirl around base to form a thin pancake. Cook for 2 minutes or until batter has set.

5 Slide pancake onto a serving plate and repeat to make three more pancakes.

6 Serve pancakes with lettuce, prawns, cucumber, carrot, sprouts, herbs and chilli dipping sauce.

CHILLI DIPPING SAUCE Place the water, juice and sugar in a small bowl; stir until sugar has dissolved. Add remaining ingredients; stir to combine.

tips This traditional Vietnamese lunch is eaten by tearing off a piece of pancake and placing it inside a lettuce leaf, along with some herbs, sprouts, prawns and vegetables; it is then rolled up and dipped into a sauce. Use a vegetable peeler to slice thin ribbons from the cucumber and carrot.

avocado and trout with fennel tzatziki

PREP + COOK TIME 10 MINUTES **SERVES** 2

Cut a lebanese cucumber in half crossways; cut one half into ribbons using a vegetable peeler. Coarsely grate remaining cucumber and squeeze out excess moisture; combine in a bowl with 2 tablespoons low-fat plain yoghurt and 1 teaspoon ground fennel. Top 2 slices of toasted soy and linseed sourdough evenly with half a small sliced avocado, cucumber ribbons and 60g (2 ounces) smoked trout slices. Drizzle with fennel tzatziki.

tip Grind fennel seeds in a mortar and pestle or a mini food processor, if ground fennel is unavailable.

chicken and pumpkin open sandwich

PREP + COOK TIME 30 MINUTES **SERVES** 2

Preheat oven to 220°C/425°F. Line an oven tray with baking paper. Place 200g (6½ ounces) coarsely chopped pumpkin onto tray. Spray with cooking oil and sprinkle with 1 teaspoon dukkah. Bake for 25 minutes or until tender; mash roughly with a fork. Top 2 slices toasted wholemeal sourdough with pumpkin, 20g (¾ ounce) baby spinach leaves and 125g (4 ounces) sliced smoked chicken breast. Drizzle with combined ½ teaspoon macadamia oil and ½ teaspoon dukkah.

nutritional count per serving

▶ 11.9g total fat	▶ 17.1g protein
▶ 2.4g saturated fat	▶ 5.3g fibre
▶ 1391kJ (332 cal)	▶ 436mg sodium
▶ 36.2g carbohydrate	▶ low GI

nutritional count per serving

▶ 10.1g total fat	▶ 26.4g protein
▶ 2g saturated fat	▶ 7.7g fibre
▶ 1514kJ (362 cal)	▶ 405mg sodium
▶ 37.3g carbohydrate	▶ low GI

mushroom and labne sandwich

PREP + COOK TIME 15 MINUTES **SERVES** 2

Roughly chop 80g (2½ ounces) each swiss brown and button mushrooms. Lightly spray a large non-stick frying pan with cooking oil. Cook mushrooms, 1 crushed garlic clove and 2 teaspoons fresh thyme leaves, over medium heat, for 5 minutes or until browned. Top 2 thin slices of seeded sourdough bread with 2 tablespoons labne, the mushroom mixture, 2 radicchio leaves and an extra 1 tablespoon of labne; drizzle with 2 teaspoons of olive oil.

tip Labne is a cheese made from strained yoghurt. You can find it at specialty food stores.

middle-eastern egg and cheese sandwich

PREP TIME 10 MINUTES **MAKES** 2

Mash 2 hard-boiled eggs with a fork in a medium bowl. Stir in ¼ cup reduced-fat cottage cheese and 1 tablespoon pistachio dukkah. Top 2 slices of toasted rye sourdough with egg mixture, 25g (¾ ounce) watercress sprigs and ¼ thinly sliced small red onion.

tips We've used dukkah but you could add curry powder instead for a classic egg sandwich. Pistachio dukkah is available from most major supermarkets in the spice aisle.
Store remaining watercress in the fridge with its stems in water, like flowers, for 2 days.

nutritional count per serving
- ▶ 10.6g total fat
- ▶ 2.1g saturated fat
- ▶ 1313kJ (314 cal)
- ▶ 39.5g carbohydrate
- ▶ 11.5g protein
- ▶ 6.9g fibre
- ▶ 413mg sodium
- ▶ low GI

nutritional count per sandwich
- ▶ 10.1g total fat
- ▶ 2.7g saturated fat
- ▶ 1418kJ (339 cal)
- ▶ 39.7g carbohydrate
- ▶ 19.3g protein
- ▶ 5g fibre
- ▶ 447mg sodium
- ▶ low GI

DINNER

sticky chicken with noodles

PREP + COOK TIME 15 MINUTES **SERVES** 2

250g (8 ounces) chicken thigh fillets, trimmed, sliced thickly

½ teaspoon chinese five-spice powder

2 teaspoons brown sugar

1 tablespoon sweet chilli sauce

2 teaspoons salt-reduced soy sauce

2 teaspoons olive oil

60g (2 ounces) bean thread vermicelli

300g (9½ ounces) gai lan, trimmed, cut into 5cm (2-inch) lengths

2 tablespoons water

2 green onions (scallions), sliced thinly

2 tablespoons fresh coriander leaves (cilantro)

1 teaspoon sesame seeds, toasted

1 Combine chicken with spice, sugar and half of the sauces in a medium bowl.

2 Heat oil in a wok over high heat; stir-fry chicken mixture, in batches, until chicken is browned and sticky. Remove from wok. Wipe wok clean.

3 Meanwhile, place noodles in a large heatproof bowl, cover with boiling water; stand for 5 minutes or until tender, drain.

4 Add gai lan to wok with the water; stir-fry for 1 minute or until just tender. Add remaining sauces; stir-fry for 1 minute or until heat through. Add noodles to wok; toss until just combined.

5 Top noodles with chicken; sprinkle with onion, coriander and sesame seeds to serve.

tips Swap bean thread vermicelli for rice stick noodles. Chicken can be marinated a day ahead; store, covered, in the fridge.

nutritional count per serving
- ▶ 14.8g total fat
- ▶ 3.6g saturated fat
- ▶ 1557kJ (372 cal)
- ▶ 29g carbohydrate
- ▶ 28.2g protein
- ▶ 5.3g fibre
- ▶ 449mg sodium
- ▶ low GI

stir-fried beef and brown rice with carrot and cucumber pickle

PREP + COOK TIME 20 MINUTES **SERVES** 2

250g (8-ounce) packet microwave brown rice

1 tablespoon olive oil

2 eggs, beaten lightly

1 clove garlic, crushed

1 tablespoon grated fresh ginger

200g (6½ ounces) lean minced (ground) beef

2 teaspoons oyster sauce

2 cups (160g) shredded cabbage

2 tablespoons shredded fresh mint leaves

1 green onion (scallion), sliced thinly

CARROT AND CUCUMBER PICKLE

⅓ cup (80ml) rice wine vinegar

2 tablespoons caster (superfine) sugar

¼ teaspoon dried chilli flakes

1 small carrot (70g), cut into matchsticks

1 lebanese cucumber (130g), seeded, cut into matchsticks

1 Cook rice according to packet instructions. Make carrot and cucumber pickle.

2 Heat 1 teaspoon of the oil in a wok over high heat; add half the egg, swirl wok to make a thin omelette. Cook, uncovered, until egg is just set. Remove from wok; roll tightly, cut into thick strips. Repeat process with another 1 teaspoon of the oil and remaining egg. Roll tightly; cut into thin strips.

3 Heat remaining oil in wok; stir-fry garlic and ginger until fragrant. Add mince; cook, stirring, until beef is browned. Add sauce; stir-fry until heated through. Remove from wok.

4 Stir-fry cabbage in wok, adding a little water if needed, until tender. Return beef to wok with rice and mint; stir-fry until hot.

5 Drain carrot and cucumber pickle; serve rice topped with pickle, omelette and onion.

CARROT AND CUCUMBER PICKLE Combine vinegar, sugar and chilli flakes in a small bowl; stir until sugar dissolves. Add carrot and cucumber; toss gently to combine.

tips Omit the rice and serve the beef and pickle mixtures in lettuce leaves, if you like. To cook your own brown rice you will need to boil ¾ cup (150g) brown rice in water for 25 minutes or until tender; drain well.

nutritional count per serving
▶ 21.8g total fat
▶ 6.1g saturated fat
▶ 2339kJ (559 cal)
▶ 51.5g carbohydrate
▶ 35.5g protein
▶ 6.7g fibre
▶ 414mg sodium
▶ medium GI

nutritional count per serving
▶ 16.9g total fat
▶ 4.3g saturated fat
▶ 1743kJ (416 cal)
▶ 41g carbohydrate
▶ 19.7g protein
▶ 10.7g fibre
▶ 265mg sodium
▶ low GI

mushroom, cavolo nero and quinoa risotto

PREP + COOK TIME 40 MINUTES **SERVES** 2

10g (½ ounce) dried porcini mushrooms

½ cup (125ml) boiling water

1 tablespoon olive oil

1 small brown onion (80g), chopped finely

1 flat mushroom (80g), chopped coarsely

100g (3 ounces) swiss brown mushrooms, sliced thinly

2 cloves garlic, crushed

½ cup quinoa (100g), rinsed, drained

2½ cups (625ml) homemade vegetable stock (see inside back flap)

1 sprig fresh thyme

100g (3 ounces) cavolo nero, sliced thinly

⅓ cup (25g) finely grated parmesan

1 Place porcini mushrooms in a heatproof bowl; cover with the boiling water. Stand for 5 minutes.
2 Meanwhile, heat oil in a medium frying pan over medium heat; cook onion, stirring, for 3 minutes or until soft. Add flat and swiss brown mushrooms; cook, stirring, for 3 minutes or until browned and tender. Add garlic; cook, stirring, for 1 minute or until fragrant.
3 Stir in quinoa, stock and thyme. Remove porcini mushrooms from water (reserve the soaking liquid); chop coarsely. Add mushrooms and soaking liquid to pan. Bring to the boil; simmer, uncovered for 20 minutes until liquid is absorbed and quinoa is tender. Discard thyme.
4 Add cavolo nero; stir until wilted. Remove pan from heat; stir through half the parmesan.
5 Serve risotto topped with remaining parmesan.

tips Cavolo nero is also known as tuscan cabbage; it is highly nutritious, and is also great to use in soups, salads and stir-fries. If using packaged vegetable stock, use a reduced-salt variety – but be careful as the sodium level may still be quite high.

indian-spiced patties with carrot raita

PREP + COOK TIME 30 MINUTES SERVES 2

420g (13½ ounce) canned no-added salt chickpeas (garbanzo beans), rinsed, drained

1 fresh long green chilli, chopped coarsely

¼ cup firmly packed fresh mint leaves

1½ teaspoons ground cumin

½ teaspoon ground cinnamon

1 clove garlic, crushed

1 teaspoon grated fresh ginger

2 tablespoons water

cooking-oil spray

30g (1 ounce) baby spinach leaves

1 wholemeal pitta bread (80g), warmed

2 lemon wedges

CARROT RAITA

½ cup (140g) low-fat plain yoghurt

½ teaspoon ground cumin

½ small carrot (35g), grated

1 Make carrot raita.

2 Blend or process chickpeas, chilli, mint, cumin, cinnamon, garlic, ginger and the water until just smooth. Shape two level tablespoons of mixture into patties.

3 Lightly spray a large non-stick frying pan with oil; cook patties, over medium heat, for 3 minutes each side or until browned and heated through.

4 Serve patties with the spinach, pitta bread, lemon wedges and raita.

CARROT RAITA Combine ingredients in a small bowl.

tip If the pattie mixture looks dry when you process it, test it by pinching the mixture with your fingers – it should hold together.

nutritional count per serving
- 6g total fat
- 20g protein
- 0.6g saturated fat
- 5.5g fibre
- 1545kJ (369 cal)
- 275mg sodium
- 55.6g carbohydrate
- low GI

five-spice beef with wasabi sauce

PREP + COOK TIME 20 MINUTES SERVES 2

2 x 125g (4-ounce) beef eye fillet steaks

1 teaspoon chinese five-spice powder

2 teaspoons olive oil

300g (9½ ounces) gai lan, halved crossways

2 teaspoons salt-reduced soy sauce

1 cup (165g) packaged microwave brown basmati rice

2 lime wedges

WASABI SAUCE

½ cup (140g) low-fat plain yoghurt

½ teaspoon wasabi paste

½ clove garlic, crushed

3 teaspoons lime juice

1 Make the wasabi sauce.

2 Coat steaks in combined five-spice and oil. Cook on a heated grill plate (or grill or barbecue) for 3 minutes each side or until cooked as desired. Cover; rest for 5 minutes.

3 Cook gai lan stems in a saucepan of boiling water for 3 minutes. Add the leaves; cook for 1 minute or until tender, drain.

4 Microwave rice until hot. Serve steaks with rice and gai lan; drizzle soy sauce over gai lan and accompany with lime wedges and wasabi sauce.

WASABI SAUCE Combine ingredients in a small bowl.

tips You can add more or less wasabi to the sauce depending on your heat preference – watch the sodium level if adding extra. Raw brown basmati rice can be difficult to find, though both major supermarkets stock the microwave brands. If cooking your own rice, you will need ½ cup uncooked brown basmati rice.

nutritional count per serving
▶ 13.6g total fat
▶ 3.8g saturated fat
▶ 1679kJ (401 cal)
▶ 27.3g carbohydrate
▶ 39g protein
▶ 6g fibre
▶ 320mg sodium
▶ medium GI

jerk salmon with black bean salad

PREP + COOK TIME 25 MINUTES SERVES 2

1 teaspoon ground coriander

½ teaspoon dried thyme

¼ teaspoon each ground cinnamon, chilli powder and allspice

1 clove garlic, crushed

2 x 100g (3-ounce) salmon fillets, skin and bones removed

1 trimmed cob corn (250g)

cooking-oil spray

½ cup (100g) canned black beans, rinsed, drained

100g (3 ounces) cherry tomatoes, halved

½ small avocado (100g), chopped coarsely

1 green onion (scallion), sliced thinly

½ cup loosely packed fresh coriander leaves (cilantro)

2 teaspoons olive oil

2 teaspoons lime juice

1 Combine ground coriander, dried thyme, cinnamon, chilli, allspice and garlic in a small bowl; rub all over salmon.

2 Meanwhile, cook corn in boiling water for 6 minutes or until tender. Drain; cool.

3 Lightly spray a large non-stick frying pan with oil. Cook salmon, over medium heat, for 3 minutes each side or until just cooked.

4 Meanwhile, remove kernels from corn. Combine corn with beans, tomato, avocado, onion, coriander and combined olive oil and lime juice in a large bowl.

5 Serve salmon with salad; accompany with lime wedges, if you like.

tips Add more chilli powder to the spice mix if you like it hot. Black beans are available from specialty food stores. You can substitute kidney or cannellini beans, if you like – just be aware the sodium level of canned beans can be high, try to buy low-sodium wherever possible.

nutritional count per serving
- 22.3g total fat
- 4.6g saturated fat
- 1819kJ (434 cal)
- 27g carbohydrate
- 25.5g protein
- 13g fibre
- 52mg sodium
- low GI

chicken, minted pea and ricotta meatballs

PREP + COOK TIME 50 MINUTES **SERVES** 2

⅓ cup (40g) frozen peas

1 teaspoon finely grated lemon rind

2 tablespoons roughly chopped fresh mint leaves

175g (5½ ounces) minced (ground) chicken

1 clove garlic, crushed

¼ cup (25g) dried multigrain breadcrumbs

1 egg yolk

2 tablespoons low-fat ricotta

1 tablespoon olive oil

400g (12½ ounces) canned diced tomatoes

2 teaspoons balsamic vinegar

130g (4 ounces) wholemeal spaghetti

2 tablespoons fresh mint leaves, extra

2 tablespoons shaved parmesan

1 Preheat oven to 240°C/475°F. Grease and line a small shallow baking dish with baking paper.

2 Place the peas in a medium heatproof bowl, cover with boiling water; stand for 1 minute, drain, reserving 1 tablespoon of the water. Blend or process peas, reserved water, rind and chopped mint until just combined.

3 Combine chicken, garlic, breadcrumbs and egg yolk in a medium bowl, mix well. Stir in pea mixture and ricotta.

4 Roll level tablespoons of mixture into balls using wet hands. Place in prepared dish; drizzle with oil. Roast for 15 minutes, turning once. Add tomato and vinegar; cook for 5 minutes or until the meatballs are cooked through and sauce is hot.

5 Meanwhile, cook pasta in a large saucepan of boiling water until tender. Drain.

6 Serve pasta with meatballs and sauce. Top with extra mint and cheese.

tip You can make the meatballs ahead of time and freeze them raw or cooked. Defrost the meatballs in the fridge before cooking.

nutritional count per serving
▶ 24.1g total fat
▶ 6.9g saturated fat
▶ 2622kJ (626 cal)
▶ 62.1g carbohydrate
▶ 40g protein
▶ 6.8g fibre
▶ 445mg sodium
▶ low GI

spanish pork cutlets

PREP + COOK TIME 1 HOUR SERVES 2

1 small kumara (orange sweet potato) (250g), cut into wedges

1 medium red capsicum (bell pepper) (200g), chopped coarsely

200g (6½ ounces) brussels sprouts, halved

1 large red onion (300g), cut into wedges

3 cloves garlic, unpeeled

1 teaspoon smoked paprika

2 teaspoons olive oil

1 medium tomato (150g), quartered

2 pork cutlets (470g), trimmed

200g (6½ ounces) green beans, trimmed

1 tablespoon roasted almond kernels

1 Preheat oven to 220°C/425°F.

2 Combine kumara, capsicum, brussels sprouts, onion and garlic in a large baking dish; sprinkle with paprika and drizzle with half the oil. Toss vegetables to coat. Bake for 40 minutes or until vegetables are golden and tender; add tomato to dish 10 minutes before end of cooking time.

3 Meanwhile, brush pork with remaining oil. Cook pork on a heated grill plate (or grill or barbecue) for 4 minutes each side or until cooked as you like. Remove from heat; cover, rest for 5 minutes.

4 Boil, steam or microwave beans until tender; cover to keep warm.

5 Squeeze garlic from skin. Blend or process garlic, tomato, nuts and half the capsicum until mixture is smooth.

6 Serve pork with roasted vegetables, beans and roasted tomato and almond sauce.

tip Make sure the sauce is hot before serving. If not, reheat it for 1 minute in a microwave-proof dish in a microwave on HIGH (100%). This sauce would also go well with roasted chicken. Double this recipe for an easy but impressive dinner for friends.

nutritional count per serving
▶ 11.9g total fat
▶ 1.9g saturated fat
▶ 1965kJ (469 cal)
▶ 34.3g carbohydrate
▶ 47.4g protein
▶ 15.6g fibre
▶ 166mg sodium
▶ low GI

miso broth with salmon and soba

PREP + COOK TIME 25 MINUTES SERVES 2

70g (2½ ounces) soba noodles

1 teaspoon sesame oil

¾ teaspoon white miso paste

2 cups (500ml) water

50g (1½ ounces) snow peas, sliced thinly

100g (3 ounces) baby spinach leaves

100g (3 ounces) enoki mushrooms, trimmed

120g (4 ounces) sashimi grade salmon, sliced thinly across the grain

1 teaspoon sesame seeds, toasted

1 green onion (scallion), sliced thinly

1 Cook noodles in simmering water for 3 minutes; drain. Rinse under cold water; drain. Toss noodles with oil in a small bowl.

2 Combine miso and the water in a small saucepan; stir over high heat until mixture just comes to the boil. Remove from heat.

3 Divide noodles, snow peas, spinach, mushrooms and salmon evenly between two serving bowls; pour over the hot broth. Sprinkle with seeds and shallots; serve immediately.

tips You can sear the salmon on all sides and finely slice it before adding it to the soup. The salmon can be substituted with tuna or ocean trout.

nutritional count per serving
- ▶ 11.8g total fat
- ▶ 2.5g saturated fat
- ▶ 1372kJ (328 cal)
- ▶ 27.2g carbohydrate
- ▶ 25.5g protein
- ▶ 5.3g fibre
- ▶ 448mg sodium
- ▶ low GI

salmon parcels with kipfler potatoes

PREP + COOK TIME 50 MINUTES SERVES 2

300g (9½ ounces) kipfler potatoes (fingerlings), sliced thinly

1 small red onion, cut into wedges

2 teaspoons olive oil

½ lemon (70g), sliced thinly

1 small tomato (90g), sliced thinly

2 x 150g (9½-ounce) salmon fillets, skin and bones removed

2 teaspoons baby capers, rinsed, drained

1 teaspoon fennel seeds

100g (3 ounces) baby spinach leaves

¼ cup firmly packed fresh parsley leaves

1 Preheat oven to 200°C/400°F.

2 Combine potatoes and onion in a medium baking dish; drizzle with half the oil. Roast for 30 minutes or until browned lightly and tender.

3 Meanwhile, arrange lemon and tomato on two 30cm-square (12-inch square) pieces of baking paper; top with salmon, capers and seeds, drizzle with remaining oil. Fold paper into a parcel to enclose salmon; place on a baking tray. Bake for 8 minutes or until salmon is cooked as you like.

4 Toss spinach through potato mixture.

5 Serve fish with potatoes and spinach and top with parsley.

tips Baking the salmon in a parcel means all the flavours, juices and steam are locked in to give a moist and tasty end result. You could try this recipe with firm white fish fillets or even chicken breast. The cooking time will vary depending on the thickness of the cut. You could also try the low-GI Carisma potatoes for this recipe.

nutritional count per serving

- ▶ 15.6g total fat
- ▶ 3.1g saturated fat
- ▶ 1642kJ (392 cal)
- ▶ 23.2g carbohydrate
- ▶ 35.5g protein
- ▶ 5g fibre
- ▶ 120mg sodium
- ▶ high GI

test kitchen tips

To cook your own brown rice you will need to boil ¾ cup (150g) brown rice in water for about 25 minutes or until tender; drain well. Don't cut the beef into thin strips or it will overcook and become tough. You could make this stir-fry with lamb instead of beef.

pepper beef stir-fry with brussels sprouts

PREP + COOK TIME 30 MINUTES SERVES 2

1 tablespoon peanut oil

200g (6½ ounces) brussels sprouts, halved

⅓ cup (80ml) water

1 medium red capsicum (bell pepper) (200g), sliced thinly

3 green onions (scallions), sliced thickly

4 cloves garlic, sliced thinly

250g (7 ounces) beef rump steak, trimmed, cut into 1cm (½-inch) slices

100g (3 ounces) roughly chopped buk choy leaves

1½ tablespoons hoisin sauce

1 tablespoon water, extra

½ teaspoon freshly ground black pepper

250g (8-ounce) packet microwave brown rice

1 Heat 1 teaspoon of the oil in a wok over high heat; stir-fry brussels sprouts for 4 minutes or until browned lightly. Add the water; cook, covered, over medium heat, for 5 minutes or until bright green and just tender. Remove from pan; cover to keep warm.

2 Wipe wok clean. Heat 1 teaspoon of the oil over high heat; stir-fry capsicum and onion for 3 minutes or until browned lightly. Add garlic; stir-fry 1 minute. Add mixture to brussels sprouts; cover to keep warm.

3 Wipe wok clean. Heat remaining oil over high heat; stir-fry beef, in two batches, for 1 minute or until browned. Return vegetables to wok with buk choy, sauce, extra water and pepper; stir-fry 1 minute or until hot.

4 Serve stir-fry with brown rice.

nutritional count per serving
▶ 17.8g total fat
▶ 4.7g saturated fat
▶ 2307kJ (551 cal)
▶ 52.5g carbohydrate
▶ 38.6g protein
▶ 12.7g fibre
▶ 388mg sodium
▶ medium GI

turkish chicken kebabs

PREP + COOK TIME 30 MINUTES (+ REFRIGERATION) **SERVES** 2

1 cup (280g) low-fat plain yoghurt

1 clove garlic, crushed

1 teaspoon ground cumin

300g (9½ ounces) chicken thigh fillets, trimmed, cut into 3cm (1¼-inch) cubes

2 tablespoons fresh flat-leaf parsley leaves

TOMATO WHEAT PILAF

2 teaspoons olive oil

1 small brown onion (80g), chopped finely

¾ cup (120g) cracked wheat

1½ cups (325ml) water

1 tablespoon salt-reduced tomato paste

CUCUMBER SALAD

½ lebanese cucumber (65g), sliced thinly

1 medium tomato (150g), sliced thinly

¼ small red onion (25g), sliced thinly

1 Combine yoghurt and garlic in a shallow bowl; reserve half the mixture. Stir cumin into remaining yoghurt mixture; add chicken, rub all over to coat in mixture. Cover, refrigerate for 30 minutes.

2 Meanwhile, make tomato wheat pilaf and cucumber salad.

3 Thread chicken equally onto 4 small skewers. Cook chicken on a heated oiled grill plate (or grill or barbecue) for 8 minutes, turning occasionally, or until cooked through.

4 Serve chicken skewers with cucumber salad, reserved garlic yoghurt, tomato wheat pilaf and parsley leaves.

TOMATO WHEAT PILAF Heat oil in a medium saucepan over medium-high heat; cook onion, stirring, for 3 minutes or until softened. Stir in wheat, the water and paste. Bring to the boil, then reduce heat; simmer, covered, for 15 minutes or until liquid is absorbed. Remove from heat; stand, covered, for 10 minutes.

CUCUMBER SALAD Combine ingredients in a small bowl.

nutritional count per serving
▸ 13.7g total fat
▸ 3.2g saturated fat
▸ 2095kJ (500 cal)
▸ 47g carbohydrate
▸ 40.5g protein
▸ 10.3g fibre
▸ 184mg sodium
▸ low GI

tips This easy cracked wheat pilaf is a great side for any barbecued meat or fish. If reheating leftover pilaf, add a little boiling water as it tends to thicken when standing. You can marinate the chicken a day ahead; store, covered, in the fridge. You could add some ground coriander and a pinch of ground chilli to the marinade.

japanese-style pork and vegetable soup

PREP + COOK TIME 15 MINUTES SERVES 2

2 teaspoons canola oil

120g (4 ounces) lean minced (ground) pork

3 teaspoons instant dashi

1 small carrot (70g), cut into matchsticks

½ small brown onion (40g), sliced thinly

60g (1½ ounces) green beans, trimmed, cut into 3cm (1¼-inch) lengths

1 litre (4 cups) water

50g (1½ ounces) small daikon, cut into matchsticks

40g (1½ ounce) fresh shiitake mushrooms, stems removed, sliced thinly

1 fresh small red thai chilli (serrano), sliced thinly

60g (2 ounces) dried rice stick noodles

1 teaspoon sesame oil

1 Heat oil in a medium saucepan over medium heat; cook pork, stirring, for 5 minutes or until cooked.
2 Add dashi, carrot, onion, beans and the water; increase heat to high. Bring to the boil, then reduce heat; simmer for 3 minutes. Add daikon, mushroom and chilli, stir to combine; remove from heat.
3 Meanwhile, cook noodles in a medium saucepan of boiling water according to packet directions; drain.
4 Divide noodles between bowls; top with soup, then drizzle with sesame oil.

tip Swap pork for chicken if you like.

nutritional count per serving
▶ 13.2g total fat
▶ 2.7g saturated fat
▶ 1248kJ (298 cal)
▶ 25.2g carbohydrate
▶ 17.4g protein
▶ 4.5g fibre
▶ 403mg sodium
▶ medium GI

ribollita

PREP + COOK TIME 1 HOUR (+ STANDING) SERVES 2

100g (3 ounces) dried cannellini beans

2 tablespoons extra-virgin olive oil

1 medium carrot (120g), cut into 1cm
(½-inch) pieces

1 small red onion (100g), cut into 1cm
(½-inch) pieces

1 trimmed celery stalk (100g), cut into 1cm
(½-inch) pieces

1 clove garlic, sliced finely

4 large roma (egg) tomatoes (360g), seeded,
cut into 1cm (½-inch) pieces

2 medium silver beet leaves (swiss chard)
(130g), white stem removed, chopped coarsely

3½ cups (875ml) water

50g (1½ ounce) rye sourdough, crust removed,
torn into bite-size pieces

2 tablespoons finely grated parmesan

1 Place beans in a medium bowl, cover with water; stand overnight. Drain; rinse under cold water, drain. Cook beans in a medium saucepan of boiling water for 40 minutes or until tender. Drain.
2 Meanwhile, heat half the oil in a medium saucepan over low heat; add carrot, onion, celery and garlic. Cook, stirring occasionally, for 20 minutes or until vegetables are softened. Stir in tomato.
3 Increase heat to medium; simmer for 10 minutes.
4 Mash half the cannellini beans with a fork; add to saucepan with remaining beans, silver beet and the water. Simmer for 20 minutes. Remove from heat; fold through bread.
5 Serve soup with parmesan; drizzle with the remaining oil.

tips Fold the bread through the hot soup just before serving – this style of soup is very thick. The soup, without the bread, can be made a day ahead; store, covered, in the fridge. You can replace the dried beans with rinsed and drained canned beans; just be aware that canned beans are high in sodium.

nutritional count per serving
▶ 22.2g total fat
▶ 4.5g saturated fat
▶ 1767kJ (422 cal)
▶ 33.1g carbohydrate
▶ 17.5g protein
▶ 15g fibre
▶ 309mg sodium
▶ low GI

kitchari

PREP + COOK TIME 40 MINUTES SERVES 2

Kitchari, an ancient Indian dish, is often eaten to detoxify the body, and is believed to aid digestion. It is based on the practise of Ayurveda, which focuses on the body's overall balance and harmony.

1 tablespoon olive oil

2 teaspoons grated fresh ginger

2 cloves garlic, crushed

3 whole cloves

½ teaspoon cumin seeds

½ fresh long green chilli, sliced finely

1 fresh bay leaf

½ small kumara (orange sweet potato) (125g), peeled, cut into 1cm (½-inch) pieces

¼ cup (30g) frozen peas

½ cup (100g) basmati rice

1½ cups (375ml) water

½ teaspoon salt-reduced chicken stock powder

½ cup (85g) rinsed, drained canned brown lentils

¼ cup (70g) low-fat plain yoghurt

2 tablespoons fresh coriander leaves (cilantro)

1 Heat oil in a medium saucepan over low heat; cook ginger, garlic, cloves, seeds, chilli and bay leaf, stirring occasionally, for 1 minute or until fragrant.
2 Stir kumara, peas, rice, the water and stock powder into pan. Shake the pan to evenly settle the rice; bring to the boil. Reduce heat; cover, simmer, without stirring, for 15 minutes.
3 Remove from heat; stand, covered, for 10 minutes, then fold through the lentils. Serve rice mixture topped with yoghurt and coriander.

tip Kitchari can be served as a breakfast dish with a poached egg and wholemeal flatbread.

nutritional count per serving

▶ 10g total fat	▶ 9.7g protein
▶ 1.5g saturated fat	▶ 4.7g fibre
▶ 1542kJ (368 cal)	▶ 375mg sodium
▶ 56.8g carbohydrate	▶ low GI

grilled steak with salsa verde and soft polenta

PREP + COOK TIME 40 MINUTES **SERVES** 2

2⅓ cups (580ml) water

½ cup (85g) polenta

1 tablespoon finely grated parmesan

2 x 120g (4-ounce) lean beef eye-fillet steaks

SALSA VERDE

¼ cup firmly packed fresh flat-leaf parsley leaves

2 tablespoons fresh mint leaves

¼ cup firmly packed fresh basil leaves

2 teaspoons rinsed, drained capers

1 clove garlic, crushed

2 teaspoons finely grated lemon rind

1½ tablespoons olive oil

1 Make salsa verde.

2 Boil the water in a medium saucepan. Gradually add polenta, stirring constantly. Reduce heat; simmer, stirring, for 10 minutes or until polenta thickens. Add cheese, stir until cheese melts. Fold through half the salsa verde; cover to keep warm.

3 Meanwhile, cook beef on a heated oiled grill plate (or grill or barbecue) for 4 minutes each side or until browned and cooked as desired. Cover; rest for 5 minutes then slice beef thickly on an angle.

4 Serve beef with polenta; accompany with remaining salsa verde.

SALSA VERDE Blend or process parsley, mint, basil, capers, garlic and rind until a coarse paste forms. Transfer to a small bowl; stir in oil to combine.

tip The polenta will firm on standing, so stir in a little hot water to loosen the mixture.

nutritional count per serving
- 23.3g total fat
- 6.3g saturated fat
- 1496kJ (357 cal)
- 32.2g carbohydrate
- 31.7g protein
- 5.4g fibre
- 148mg sodium
- medium GI

grilled pork with sicilian-style caponata

PREP + COOK TIME 35 MINUTES **SERVES** 2

Caponata is a warm vegetable salad often made with eggplant.

300g (9½ ounces) kipfler potatoes (fingerlings), halved lengthways

1 teaspoon olive oil

1 small eggplant (230g), chopped coarsely

½ small red onion, (50g), chopped finely

2 cloves garlic, sliced thinly

1 tablespoon red wine vinegar

2 medium tomatoes (300g), chopped coarsely

⅓ cup (40g) seeded green olives

2 teaspoons rinsed, drained baby capers

¼ cup fresh flat-leaf parsley

300g (9½ ounces) pork fillet

1 tablespoon coarsely chopped roasted almonds

1 Boil, steam or microwave potatoes until just tender; drain.

2 Meanwhile, heat oil in a medium frying pan over medium heat; cook eggplant, stirring, for 5 minutes or until browned and softened. Add onion and garlic; cook, stirring, for 3 minutes or until onion softens.

3 Add vinegar and tomato to pan; bring to the boil. Reduce heat; simmer, uncovered, for 10 minutes or until tomato softens. Stir in olives, capers and parsley.

4 Meanwhile, cook pork on a heated oiled grill plate (or grill or barbecue) for 10 minutes, turning occasionally, or until cooked as desired. Cover pork; rest for 5 minutes, then slice thickly.

5 Cook potatoes, cut-side down, on a heated grill plate for 3 minutes or until heated through.

6 Serve pork with caponata and potatoes; top with nuts, and extra parsley leaves, if you like.

tip We have used kipfler potatoes in this recipe, you can use any firm variety of potato you like: pontiac, sebago, desiree and coliban are all fine.

nutritional count per serving
▶ 13.3g total fat
▶ 2.2g saturated fat
▶ 1753kJ (418 cal)
▶ 27.2g carbohydrate
▶ 41.2g protein
▶ 10g fibre
▶ 446mg sodium
▶ high GI

pumpkin tabbouleh

PREP + COOK TIME 35 MINUTES **SERVES** 2

Preheat oven to 220°C/425°F. Line an oven tray
with baking paper. Combine 200g (6½ ounces)
chopped pumpkin and half a thickly sliced small
red onion on tray; drizzle with 1 teaspoon olive oil.
Bake for 20 minutes or until tender. Cool; transfer to
a large bowl. Meanwhile, bring 1 cup water to the
boil in a small saucepan. Add ⅓ cup cracked wheat;
reduce heat, simmer, covered, for 15 minutes or
until tender. Remove from heat; stand 10 minutes.
Cool; transfer to the bowl with vegetables. Combine
½ cup fresh flat-leaf parsley and 180g (5½ ounces)
halved cherry tomatoes with pumpkin and cracked
wheat mixture. Combine 2 tablespoons lemon juice
and 1 crushed garlic clove, drizzle over tabbouleh;
toss gently to combine.

zucchini and mint couscous salad

PREP + COOK TIME 20 MINUTES **SERVES** 2

Combine ½ cup wholegrain couscous and ½ cup
boiling water in a medium bowl; cover, stand for
5 minutes, fluff with a fork occasionally. Thickly
slice 2 small zucchini; cook on a heated oiled
grill plate (or grill or barbecue) for 2 minutes
each side or until tender and browned. Combine
zucchini, couscous, ½ cup fresh mint leaves,
¼ cup crumbled reduced-fat fetta, 1 tablespoon
olive oil and 2 teaspoons each finely grated lemon
rind and lemon juice.

tip This is great as a side dish with grilled meats
or fish.

nutritional count per serving
- ▶ 5.5g total fat
- ▶ 6.3g protein
- ▶ 0.8g saturated fat
- ▶ 9.3g fibre
- ▶ 877kJ (210 cal)
- ▶ 33mg sodium
- ▶ 28.4g carbohydrate
- ▶ medium GI

nutritional count per serving
- ▶ 13.4g total fat
- ▶ 13.4g protein
- ▶ 3.7g saturated fat
- ▶ 5g fibre
- ▶ 1418kJ (339 cal)
- ▶ 285mg sodium
- ▶ 38.4g carbohydrate
- ▶ medium GI

brown rice and kale stir-fry

PREP + COOK TIME 15 MINUTES **SERVES** 2

Coarsely chop 1 medium brown onion. Coarsely chop the stalk and leaves of 100g (3 ounces) kale. Lightly spray a large non-stick frying pan with oil; cook onion and kale stalks, over medium heat, for 3 minutes. Stir in leaves, 1 cup cooked brown rice, 1 teaspoon grated fresh ginger and 2 teaspoons salt-reduced soy sauce; cook until hot. Transfer to a large bowl; cover to keep warm. Wipe pan clean. Lightly spray with cooking oil; cook 2 eggs, over low heat, until cooked. Serve rice topped with eggs. Sprinkle with ½ sliced long red chilli and 2 teaspoons toasted sesame seeds.

tip You could use basmati or doongara as an alternative to brown rice. You will need ½ cup (100g) uncooked brown rice for this recipe.

nutritional count per serving
- ▶ 10.9g total fat
- ▶ 12.8g protein
- ▶ 2.4g saturated fat
- ▶ 5g fibre
- ▶ 1226kJ (293 cal)
- ▶ 258mg sodium
- ▶ 33.3g carbohydrate
- ▶ high GI

pearl barley salad

PREP + COOK TIME 50 MINUTES **SERVES** 2

Preheat oven to 220°C/425°F. Peel and cut 1 large beetroot (beet) and 1 medium brown onion into wedges; place on a large oven tray; drizzle with 2 teaspoons olive oil. Roast for 20 minutes. Add 200g (6½ ounces) broccoli florets; roast a further 15 minutes or until golden and tender. Cook ½ cup pearl barley in a medium saucepan of boiling water for 40 minutes or until tender; drain well. Combine 1 tablespoon each of tahini, warm water and lemon juice in a small bowl. Toss roasted vegetables and ½ cup fresh flat-leaf parsley through warm barley. Drizzle with tahini dressing to serve.

tips You could also use fresh mint or coriander. The salad tastes just as good at room temperature, so any leftovers will make a great packed lunch.

nutritional count per serving
- ▶ 12.3g total fat
- ▶ 14.7g protein
- ▶ 1.6g saturated fat
- ▶ 16.9g fibre
- ▶ 1576kJ (377 cal)
- ▶ 113mg sodium
- ▶ 43g carbohydrate
- ▶ low GI

DESSERT

spelt crêpes with rhubarb in rose syrup

PREP + COOK TIME 40 MINUTES (+ REFRIGERATION) SERVES 2

⅓ cup (50g) white spelt flour

⅓ cup (80ml) skim milk

1 tablespoon grape-seed oil

1 egg white

1 teaspoon low-GI cane sugar

175g (5½ ounces) trimmed rhubarb, cut into 3cm (1¼-inch) lengths

1 tablespoon rose syrup

cooking-oil spray

½ cup (140g) low-fat plain yoghurt

1 Preheat grill (broiler). Line oven tray with baking paper.

2 Place flour, milk, oil, egg white and half the sugar in a medium bowl; whisk until smooth. Cover, refrigerate 30 minutes.

3 Meanwhile, place rhubarb on tray; sprinkle with remaining sugar and drizzle with syrup. Grill for 5 minutes or until rhubarb is tender.

4 Spray a heavy-based small non-stick frying pan with oil. Heat over medium-high heat; pour a sixth of the batter into pan. Cook until browned underneath. Turn crêpe, brown the other side. Repeat with remaining batter to make a total of 6 crêpes.

5 Serve crêpes with rhubarb and yoghurt.

tips Rose syrup can be found in the international food aisle of major supermarkets or in specialty Middle-Eastern supermarkets. Substitute the rose syrup with half the amount of rose water, if you like.

nutritional count per serving
- ▶ 9.1g total fat
- ▶ 1.1g saturated fat
- ▶ 1067kJ (255 cal)
- ▶ 33g carbohydrate
- ▶ 12.2g protein
- ▶ 2.9g fibre
- ▶ 133mg sodium
- ▶ low GI

orange yoghurt cake

PREP + COOK TIME 55 MINUTES **SERVES** 12

2 eggs

¾ cup (150g) firmly packed brown sugar

2 teaspoons finely grated orange rind

¾ cup (90g) ground almonds

⅓ cup (50g) wholemeal self-raising flour

⅓ cup (95g) low-fat plain yoghurt

ORANGE CREAM CHEESE ICING

60g (2 ounces) light cream cheese, softened

2 tablespoons icing (confectioner's) sugar

1 tablespoon orange juice

1 Preheat oven to 160°C/325°F. Grease a closed 20cm/8-inch (base measurement) round springform pan; line base and side with baking paper.
2 Beat eggs, sugar and rind a small bowl with an electric mixer until light and fluffy. Stir in ground almonds, flour and yoghurt.
3 Spoon the mixture into pan; bake for about 45 minutes. Stand in pan for 5 minutes before turning, top-side up, onto a wire rack to cool.
4 Meanwhile, make orange cream cheese icing.
5 Spread cake with icing; top with thinly sliced orange rind, if you like.

ORANGE CREAM CHEESE ICING Whisk ingredients in a small bowl until smooth.

tips Swap the orange for lemon for a citrus burst. The cake can be made ahead; store in an airtight container for up to 2 days or wrap and freeze for up to 2 months.

nutritional count per serving
▶ 6.4g total fat
▶ 1.4g saturated fat
▶ 603kJ (144 cal)
▶ 17.5g carbohydrate
▶ 4g protein
▶ 1.2g fibre
▶ 64mg sodium
▶ low GI

poached pears with espresso syrup

PREP + COOK TIME 55 MINUTES SERVES 2

2 small pears (360g)

1 vanilla bean, halved lengthways

1 tablespoon dark brown sugar

½ teaspoon instant coffee granules

HAZELNUT WAFERS

1 egg white

2 tablespoons caster (superfine) sugar

1 tablespoon ground hazelnut

1 tablespoon plain (all-purpose) flour

15g (½ ounce) low-fat salt-reduced margarine, melted

1 Make hazelnut wafers.

2 Cover peeled pears with water in a medium saucepan; bring to the boil. Reduce heat; simmer, uncovered, for 30 minutes or until pears are tender.

3 Drain pears, reserving 1 cup of cooking liquid.

4 Combine reserved liquid, vanilla bean and sugar in same pan; bring to the boil, stirring. Add coffee, reduce heat to medium; simmer, uncovered, for 10 minutes or until syrup thickens slightly.

5 Drizzle syrup over pears, serve with wafers.

HAZELNUT WAFERS Preheat oven to 200°C/400°F. Combine ingredients in a small bowl. Spread mixture onto a lined oven tray to make six 11cm (4½-inch) rounds. Bake for 8 minutes or until golden and crisp around the edges. Cool on a wire rack.

tips Watch the hazelnut wafers while baking, as they can easily burn if left in the oven too long. The wafers can be made a day ahead; store in an airtight container.

nutritional count per serving
▶ 5g total fat
▶ 0.6g saturated fat
▶ 691kJ (165 cal)
▶ 27.9g carbohydrate
▶ 2.7g protein
▶ 1.5g fibre
▶ 58mg sodium
▶ medium GI

chocolate semifreddo

PREP + COOK TIME 10 MINUTES (+ FREEZING) **SERVES** 2

1 tablespoon cocoa powder

¼ cup (40g) icing (confectioners') sugar

1 egg, separated

¼ cup (70g) low-fat ricotta

100g (3 ounces) fresh mixed berries

1 Lightly grease one ¾-cup (180ml) hole of a mini loaf pan. Line base and two long sides with baking paper, extending paper 2cm (¾-inch) above edges.
2 Whisk sifted cocoa and icing sugar, egg yolk and ricotta in a small bowl until smooth.
3 Beat egg white in a small bowl with an electric mixer until soft peaks form; fold through chocolate mixture, in two batches. Spoon into pan hole. Freeze for 4 hours or overnight.
4 Remove pan from freezer 10 minutes before serving. Cut in half and serve topped with berries.

nutritional count per serving
- 5.3g total fat
- 8.8g protein
- 2.5g saturated fat
- 2.9g fibre
- 812kJ (194 cal)
- 122mg sodium
- 27.3g carbohydrate
- medium GI

nutritional count per serving

- ▸ 5g total fat
- ▸ 2g saturated fat
- ▸ 732kJ (175 cal)
- ▸ 14.6g carbohydrate
- ▸ 12.8g protein
- ▸ 8.4g fibre
- ▸ 40mg sodium
- ▸ low GI

passionfruit mousse

PREP TIME 10 MINUTES (+ REFRIGERATION) **SERVES** 2

300g (9½ ounces) silken tofu

1 tablespoon light agave syrup

1 teaspoon vanilla extract

1 teaspoon finely grated lemon rind

¼ cup (60ml) fresh passionfruit pulp

1 tablespoon fresh mint leaves

1 tablespoon fresh passionfruit pulp, extra

1 tablespoon flaked coconut, toasted

1 Blend or process tofu, syrup, vanilla and rind until smooth. Stir through passionfruit.

2 Spoon mixture into two 1-cup (250ml) serving glasses. Refrigerate for 2 hours.

3 Serve mousse topped with mint, extra passionfruit and coconut.

tip You will need about 3 passionfruit.

frozen peach lassi

PREP + COOK TIME 10 MINUTES (+ FREEZING) SERVES 4

Lassi is a yoghurt-based drink from India.

2 cups (365g) drained canned peach slices in natural juice

2 tablespoons honey

½ cup (125ml) buttermilk

1 cup (280g) low-fat plain yoghurt

2 teaspoons finely grated lime rind

2 teaspoons lime juice

1 cup (180g) canned peach slices in natural juice, extra

1 teaspoon finely grated lime rind, extra

1 Process or blend peaches until smooth.

2 Whisk peach puree with the honey, buttermilk, yoghurt, rind and juice in a large bowl.

3 Pour mixture into a 1-litre (4-cup) container. Cover tightly with foil; freeze for 3 hours or overnight.

4 Beat lassi in a large bowl with an electric mixer until smooth. Return to container, cover; freeze a further 3 hours or until firm. Alternatively, churn lassi in an ice-cream machine according to the manufacturer's instructions.

5 Serve lassi with extra peach slices and lime rind.

tip You will need a 1kg (2 pound) container of peach slices in natural juice for this recipe. You could also try this with other canned fruits such as plum or mango.

nutritional count per serving
- ▶ 0.8g total fat
- ▶ 0.5g saturated fat
- ▶ 679kJ (162 cal)
- ▶ 30.2g carbohydrate
- ▶ 6.8g protein
- ▶ 2.1g fibre
- ▶ 78mg sodium
- ▶ low GI

strawberry and orange mille feuille

PREP + COOK TIME 15 MINUTES (+ COOLING) MAKES 2

cooking-oil spray

1 sheet fillo pastry

⅓ cup (80g) low-fat ricotta

1 tablespoon icing (confectioner's) sugar

½ teaspoon finely grated orange rind

3 teaspoons orange juice

325g (8 ounces) strawberries, sliced thinly

1 Preheat oven to 200°C/400°F. Lightly spray a baking tray with oil.

2 Lightly spray pastry with oil; fold in half. Cut pastry into six rectangles. Place on tray; bake for 5 minutes or until golden. Cool.

3 Meanwhile, combine ricotta, 3 teaspoons of the sifted icing sugar, rind and juice in a bowl.

4 Place a pastry rectangle on a serving plate; lightly spread a quarter of the ricotta mixture over pastry, top with a quarter of the strawberries. Repeat layer, finishing with a third pastry rectangle.

5 Repeat step 4 to make a second mille feuille; sprinkle mille feuilles with the remaining sifted icing sugar to serve.

nutritional count per mille feuille
▶ 4.2g total fat
▶ 1.6g saturated fat
▶ 496kJ (118 cal)
▶ 10.4g carbohydrate
▶ 7.9g protein
▶ 3.1g fibre
▶ 156mg sodium
▶ low GI

test kitchen tips

To avoid the mille feuille slipping around the plate, place a dab of the ricotta mixture under the first pastry rectangle. It will hold the pastry in place. You need to assemble these mille feuilles just before serving or the pastry will go soggy. You can use any seasonal fruit such as raspberries and blueberries, thinly sliced stone fruit, or sliced seedless grapes or fresh figs.

DESSERT

coffee granita

PREP + COOK TIME 10 MINUTES (+ COOLING & FREEZING) **SERVES** 6

⅓ cup (75g) low-GI cane sugar

3 cups (750ml) water

¼ cup (60ml) strong espresso coffee

¼ cup (60ml) thickened (heavy) light cream

1 Combine sugar and the water in a small saucepan over low heat, stirring, until sugar is dissolved. Remove from heat, stir in coffee, cool to room temperature.
2 Pour coffee mixture into a shallow metal tray; cover, freeze for 6 hours, scraping with a fork every hour.
3 Scrape granita with a fork; spoon into glasses, drizzle each with 2 teaspoons of cream; serve granita immediately.

tips To make the strong espresso coffee, dissolve 3 teaspoons instant espresso coffee into ⅓ cup boiling water. This granita is a delicious alternative to regular coffee for brunch when entertaining friends in the warmer months. Use granita within 1 month of making.

nutritional count per serving
▶ 1.8g total fat
▶ 0.3g protein
▶ 1.2g saturated fat
▶ 2.9g fibre
▶ 279kJ (67 cal)
▶ 3mg sodium
▶ 12.9g carbohydrate
▶ low GI

strawberry and pomegranate custard tarts

PREP + COOK TIME 20 MINUTES SERVES 2

1 sheet fillo pastry

cooking-oil spray

⅔ cup (160ml) low-fat milk

1 egg

2 teaspoons caster (superfine) sugar

½ teaspoon vanilla extract

6 small strawberries (75g), quartered lengthways

40g (1½ ounces) fresh pomegranate seeds

1 teaspoon pomegranate molasses

1 Preheat oven to 200°C/400°F. Oil two holes of a 12-hole (⅓-cup/180ml) muffin pan.

2 Cut pastry in half crossways. Lightly spray one of the pastry halves with oil, then fold in half; cut pastry into four. Firmly press pastry strips into pan hole overlapping each other to cover hole, spray lightly with oil to stick pastry strips together. Repeat with remaining pastry.

3 Bake cases for 5 minutes or until pastry is browned lightly.

4 Meanwhile, heat milk until hot. Whisk egg, sugar and extract in a small bowl; gradually whisk in hot milk. Pour custard into pastry cases. Bake for 15 minutes or until set. Stand tarts for 5 minutes before transferring to a wire rack to cool.

5 Combine strawberries, pomegranate and molasses in a small bowl. Serve tarts topped with strawberry mixture.

tip The tarts can be made a day ahead; store in an airtight container in the fridge. Top with the strawberry mixture before serving.

---

nutritional count per serving

- ► 4.4g total fat
- ► 1g saturated fat
- ► 607kJ (145 cal)
- ► 17.2g carbohydrate
- ► 2.1g protein
- ► 2.4g fibre
- ► 124mg sodium
- ► low GI

baked apples and raspberries with quinoa almond crumble

PREP + COOK TIME 1 HOUR **SERVES** 2

2 medium pink lady apples (300g), unpeeled

50g (1½ ounces) fresh raspberries

1 teaspoon finely grated lemon rind

2 teaspoons low-GI cane sugar

CRUMBLE TOPPING

1 tablespoon quinoa flakes

2 teaspoons white spelt flour

1 tablespoon coarsely chopped roasted almonds

½ teaspoon low-GI cane sugar

1 teaspoon butter

pinch cinnamon

1 Preheat oven to 160°C/325°F. Grease and line a baking tray with baking paper.
2 Make crumble topping.
3 Core unpeeled apples about three-quarters of the way down from stem end, making the hole 4cm (1½ inches) in diameter. Use a small sharp knife to score around the centre of each apple. Make a small deep cut in the base of each apple.
4 Pack combined berries, lemon rind and sugar firmly into apples; top with crumble topping. Place apples on tray. Bake, uncovered, for 45 minutes or until apples are just tender.

CRUMBLE TOPPING Place ingredients in a small bowl; using your fingers, rub the mixture together until well combined.

serving suggestion Serve with low-fat ice-cream or yoghurt.

nutritional count per serving
▶ 5.6g total fat
▶ 1.5g saturated fat
▶ 770kJ (184 cal)
▶ 28g carbohydrate
▶ 2.3g protein
▶ 5.7g fibre
▶ 18mg sodium
▶ low GI

test kitchen tips

Use your favourite variety of apple;
we used pink lady as they have a
sweet flavour that marries well with
the raspberries. If you don't have an
apple corer, you can use a melon
baller to remove the apple core.

mixed berry clafoutis

PREP + COOK TIME 40 MINUTES **SERVES** 2

Preheat oven to 180°C/350°F. Lightly spray a
2 cup (500ml) shallow baking dish with cooking oil.
Whisk 1 egg and ¼ cup plain (all-purpose) flour
in a small bowl until combined. Whisk in ¼ cup
low-fat milk, 1½ tablespoons caster (superfine)
sugar, 1 teaspoon melted butter and 1 teaspoon
vanilla extract. Pour into dish. Top with 1 cup
frozen mixed berries. Bake for 30 minutes or until
mixture is puffed and golden. Dust with ½ teaspoon
icing (confectioners') sugar to serve.

tip You could also serve this with low-GI,
low-fat vanilla ice-cream.

nutritional count per serving	
▶ 5.6g total fat	▶ 7.4g protein
▶ 2.4g saturated fat	▶ 3.1g fibre
▶ 941kJ (245 cal)	▶ 72mg sodium
▶ 32.9g carbohydrate	▶ medium GI

raspberry and vanilla yoghurt ice-blocks

PREP + COOK TIME 25 MINUTES
(+ COOLING & FREEZING) **MAKES** 14

Combine ¼ cup low-GI cane sugar, 1 split vanilla
bean and ¾ cup water in a small saucepan; stir over
low heat for 4 minutes or until sugar is dissolved.
Bring to the boil without stirring; reduce heat, simmer
for 10 minutes or until syrupy. Remove vanilla bean;
cool. Blend cooled syrup and 300g (9½ ounces) frozen
raspberries until smooth. Very gently swirl in 2⅔ cups
low-fat plain yoghurt. Pour into fourteen ⅓-cup (80ml)
ice-block moulds. Freeze overnight or until firm.

tips Don't stir the yoghurt into the raspberry
mixture or you will lose the marbled effect. It
will swirl naturally when you pour the mixture
into the moulds. Use a skewer to swirl it once in
the moulds, if necessary. You could use frozen
strawberries, cherries or mango.

nutritional count per ice-block	
▶ 0.2g total fat	▶ 3.5g protein
▶ 0.1g saturated fat	▶ 1.3g fibre
▶ 229kJ (55 cal)	▶ 39mg sodium
▶ 8.3g carbohydrate	▶ low GI

mixed berry fool

PREP TIME 5 MINUTES (+ STANDING) **MAKES** 2

Layer 150g (6½ ounces) frozen mixed berries and
⅔-cup low-fat vanilla custard in two ¾-cup (180ml)
serving glasses. Sprinkle with 2 finely chopped
almond biscotti. Stand for 20 minutes or until
berries have thawed.

tips You can thaw the berries in the microwave
but assembling this dessert when frozen means
you get perfect layers. Assemble it before dinner
and it will be ready for dessert. You could make a
tropical fool with seeded fresh lychees and fresh
passionfruit pulp.

apple berry crumble

PREP + COOK TIME 40 MINUTES **MAKES** 2

Preheat oven to 200°C/400°F. Peel and coarsely
chopped 2 large granny smith apples. Cook apples
with 2 tablespoons water in a covered small saucepan
over medium heat for 8 minutes or until apples are
just tender. Stir through 100g (3 ounces) frozen
mixed berries. Divide between two 1-cup (250ml)
ovenproof ramekins. Rub 10g (½ ounce) canola
spread into 1 tablespoon plain (all-purpose) flour in
a small bowl until mixture resembles breadcrumbs.
Stir in 1 tablespoons rolled oats, 2 teaspoons
low-GI cane sugar and 5 chopped hazelnuts; sprinkle
over berry mixture. Bake for 25 minutes or until
crumble is golden brown.

tip This crumble topping would go well with a
pear and ginger crumble or apple and raspberry.

nutritional count per fool
▶ 1.9g total fat
▶ 0.7g saturated fat
▶ 553kJ (132 cal)
▶ 22g carbohydrate
▶ 4.9g protein
▶ 2.8g fibre
▶ 50mg sodium
▶ low GI

nutritional count per crumble
▶ 5.7g total fat
▶ 0.7g saturated fat
▶ 894kJ (214 cal)
▶ 35g carbohydrate
▶ 2.6g protein
▶ 6.5g fibre
▶ 24mg sodium
▶ low GI

COOKING TECHNIQUES

Preparing asparagus To snap the woody end off the asparagus, hold it close to the base and bend it until it snaps. Discard woody ends. Trim with a vegetable peeler.

Crushing garlic Press unpeeled garlic firmly with the flat blade of a large knife (top) crushing the clove. Pull off the papery skin and chop the clove finely with the knife. A garlic press (bottom) removes and leaves the skin behind while crushing the garlic.

Trimming beetroot Cut the stems to 2cm (¾ inch) of the bulb. Don't trim the beard at the base of the plant, as this stops the colour from bleeding during cooking.

Cutting cucumber or zucchini into thin ribbons will give long, thin, uniform slices. The best tool for this is a vegetable peeler. By applying more pressure on the peeler you will get thicker ribbons.

To remove corn from fresh cobs, remove the husk (the outer covering) and the silk (the soft silky inner threads), and trim one side of the corn cob so it lies flat. Use a large flat-bladed knife to cut down the cob, close to the core, to remove the kernels.

Slicing fennel, or cabbage, thinly is easy using a V-slicer – you simply slide the fennel back and forth across the blade. The adjustable blade is very sharp, so watch your fingers. A guard is supplied, so use it to protect your fingers from any unwanted mishaps.

To extract seeds and pulp from a pomegranate, cut in half and hold it over a bowl. Hit sharply with a spoon – the seeds (surrounded by the pulp) should fall out – if they don't, dig them out with a teaspoon. Be careful as the pomegranate juice can stain your hands, clothes and bench top.

Pitting an olive is easy with an olive pitter, pictured; put the olive in the cup and push, and out pops the seed. To do this by hand, crush the olive with the flat side of a large knife and slip the seed out.

Wrapping salmon in paper (1) (salmon parcels with kipfler potatoes p79) Cut baking paper into a 30cm (12-inch) square; top with the salmon, capers and seeds, then drizzle with oil.

Wrapping salmon in paper (2) Fold the paper so the ends meet above the fish, then fold the paper edges over together to form a parcel. This technique is known as 'en papillote'; the closed paper pouch steams the food wrapped in it.

To slice a capsicum, cut the top and bottom off the capsicum and stand it on one end; slice down removing all the flesh. Remove and discard the seeds and membranes, and slice the flesh as indicated by the recipe.

Chiffonade is a way of cutting green leaves into long, thin strips. Lay leaves flat on top of each other, then roll up tightly and cut into thin strips.

Lining a muffin tin with pastry strips (strawberry and pomegranate custard tarts p107) Cut fillo in half crossways. Lightly spray one half with oil, then fold in half; cut pastry into four. Press pastry strips into pan hole, overlapping, to cover hole, spray lightly with oil to stick pastry strips together.

To peel a prawn, hold the body with one hand, twist the head with the other and pull it away from the body. Roll the shell off from the underside with the legs still attached. If removing the tail, squeeze the tail on both sides to release the shell from the flesh and remove.

To trim green onions, pull the papery skin, towards the root, off the onion. Cut the root end off, then slice the white end of the onion as directed by the recipe. The green end can be used to garnish the dish, either thinly sliced, or curled by placing thin strips into iced water.

Hull a strawberry The hull, or calyx, is the green leafy top. Cut around the leafy top and into the pale flesh underneath, and discard. Wash and drain the strawberries before using.

GLOSSARY

AGAVE SYRUP a sweetener commercially produced from the agave plant in South Africa and Mexico. It is sweeter than sugar, though less viscous, so it dissolves quickly. Agave syrup is sold in light, amber and dark varieties.

ALL-BRAN CEREAL a low-fat, high-fibre breakfast cereal based on wheat bran.

BAKING POWDER a raising agent consisting mainly of two parts cream of tartar to one part bicarbonate of soda (baking soda).

BASIL an aromatic herb; there are many types, but the most commonly used is sweet, or common, basil.
thai also known as horapa; different from holy basil and sweet basil in both look and taste, having smaller leaves and purplish stems. It has a slight aniseed taste and is one of the identifying flavours of Thai food.

BEANS
black also known as turtle beans or black kidney beans; an earthy-flavoured bean completely different from the better-known chinese black beans (which are fermented soya beans).
broad also known as fava, windsor and horse beans. Fresh and frozen forms should be peeled twice (discarding both the outer long green pod and the beige-green tough inner shell).
cannellini small white bean similar in appearance and flavour to great northern, navy and haricot beans – all of which can be substituted for the other. Available dried or canned.
kidney medium-sized red bean, slightly floury in texture yet sweet in flavour; sold dried or canned.
sprouts also known as bean shoots; tender new growths of assorted beans and seeds grown for consumption as sprouts. The most readily available are mung bean, soya bean, alfalfa and snow pea sprouts.
white in this book, some recipes may call for 'white beans', a generic term we use for cannellini, great northern, haricot or navy beans, all of which can be substituted for the other.

BICARBONATE OF SODA also known as baking or carb soda; is used as a leavening agent in baking.

BUK CHOY also known as bok choy, pak choi, chinese white cabbage or chinese chard; has a fresh, mild mustard taste. Baby buk choy, also known as pak kat farang or shanghai bok choy, is much smaller and more tender than buk choy.

BUTTERMILK originally the term given to the slightly sour liquid left after butter was churned from cream, today it is made similarly to yogurt. Sold alongside all fresh milk products in supermarkets; despite the implication of its name, it is low in fat.

CAVOLO NERO also known as tuscan cabbage or tuscan black cabbage. It has long, narrow, wrinkled leaves and a rich and astringent, mild cabbage flavour. It doesn't lose its volume like silver beet or spinach when cooked, but it does need longer cooking. It is a member of the kale family; if you can't find it use silver beet (swiss chard) or cabbage instead.

CHEESE
cottage fresh, white, unripened curd cheese with a grainy consistency and a fat content between 5% and 15%.
cream commonly known as Philly or Philadelphia, a soft cows'-milk cheese with a fat content of at least 33%. Also available as spreadable light cream cheese, a blend of cottage and cream cheeses with a fat content of 21%.
goat made from goats' milk, has an earthy, strong taste; available in soft and firm textures, in various shapes and sizes, and sometimes rolled in ash or herbs.
mozzarella a soft, spun-curd cheese. It has a low melting point and an elastic texture when heated; used to add texture rather than flavour. A favourite cheese for pizza.
parmesan also known as parmigiano, parmesan is a hard, grainy cows'-milk cheese. The curd is salted in brine for a month before being aged for up to two years in humid conditions.

ricotta the name for this soft, white, cows'-milk cheese roughly translates as 'cooked again'. It's made from whey, a by-product of other cheese-making, to which fresh milk and acid are added.
tasty a matured cheddar; use an aged, strongly-flavoured, hard variety.

CHICKPEAS also called garbanzos, hummus or channa; an irregularly round, sandy-coloured legume.

CHILLI available in many different types and sizes. Use rubber gloves when seeding and chopping fresh chillies as they can burn your skin. Removing seeds and membranes lessens the heat level.
flakes, dried deep-red, dehydrated chilli slices and whole seeds.
long green or red available both fresh and dried; a generic term used for any moderately hot, long (about 6cm to 8cm), thin chilli.
red thai also known as 'scuds'; small, very hot and bright red in colour.

CHINESE FIVE-SPICE POWDER a fragrant mixture of ground cinnamon, cloves, star anise, sichuan pepper and fennel seeds.

CHOY SUM also known as pakaukeo or flowering cabbage, a member of the buk choy family; easy to identify with its long stems, light green leaves and yellow flowers. Is eaten, stems and all, steamed or stir-fried.

COCOA POWDER unsweetened, dried, roasted then ground cocoa beans (cacao seeds).

CORIANDER also known as pak chee, cilantro or chinese parsley; bright-green leafy herb with a pungent flavour. Both the stems and roots of coriander are used; wash well before using. Is also available ground or as seeds; these should not be substituted for fresh as the tastes are completely different.

CORNFLOUR also known as cornstarch; used as a thickening agent in cooking. Wheaten cornflour is made from wheat rather than corn and gives cakes a lighter texture (due to the fact wheaten cornflour has some gluten).

CREAM we used fresh cream, also known as pouring and pure cream, unless otherwise stated. It has no additives unlike thickened cream. Minimum fat content 35%.
sour a thick, cultured soured cream. Minimum fat content 35%.
thickened a whipping cream containing a thickener. Minimum fat content 35%.

DAIKON also known as giant white radish. Used extensively in Japanese cooking; has a sweet, fresh flavour without the bite of the common red radish.

EGGPLANT, BABY also known as finger or japanese eggplant; very small and slender.

FENNEL also known as finocchio or anise; a white to very pale green-white, firm, crisp, roundish vegetable about 8cm-12cm in diameter. The bulb has a slightly sweet, anise flavour but the leaves have a much stronger taste. Also the name given to dried seeds having a licorice flavour.

FLAT-LEAF PARSLEY also known as continental parsley or italian parsley.

FLOUR
buckwheat a herb in the same plant family as rhubarb; not a cereal so it is gluten-free.
plain a general all-purpose flour made from wheat.
rice a very fine flour, made from ground white rice.
self-raising plain flour sifted with baking powder in the proportion of 1 cup flour to 2 teaspoons baking powder. Also called self-rising flour.
spelt very similar to wheat, but has a slightly nuttier, sweeter flavour. Spelt flour contains gluten.
wholemeal milled from whole wheat grain (bran, germ and endosperm).

GAI LAN also known as chinese broccoli, gai larn, kanah, gai lum, chinese broccoli and chinese kale; appreciated more for its stems than its coarse leaves.

GINGER, FRESH also known as green or root ginger; the thick root of a tropical plant.

HARISSA a hot Moroccan sauce or paste made from dried chillies, cumin, garlic, oil and caraway seeds. The paste, available in a tube, is very hot and should not be used in large amounts; bottled harissa sauce is milder, but is still hot. If you have a low heat-level tolerance, you may find any recipe containing harissa too hot to tolerate. Available from supermarkets and Middle-Eastern grocery stores.

KAFFIR LIME LEAVES also known as bai magrood, look like two glossy dark green leaves joined end to end, forming a rounded hourglass shape. Used similarly to bay leaves or curry leaves. Sold fresh, dried or frozen; dried leaves are less potent so double the number if using them as a substitute for fresh. A strip of fresh lime peel may be substituted for each kaffir lime leaf.

MISO Japan's famous bean paste made from fermented soya beans and rice, rye or barley. It varies in colour, texture and saltiness. White miso tends to have a sweeter and somewhat less salty flavour than the darker red miso. Dissolve miso in a little water before adding. Keeps well refrigerated.

MOUNTAIN BREAD a thin, dry, soft-textured bread, that can be rolled up and filled with your favourite filling.

MUSHROOM
cup a common white mushroom picked just as the veil, or underside, begins to open around the stem. Has a full-bodied flavour and firm texture.
enoki clumps of long, spaghetti-like stems with tiny, snowy white caps.
flat large, flat mushrooms with a rich earthy flavour. They are sometimes misnamed field mushrooms, which are wild mushrooms.
porcini, dried the richest flavoured mushrooms; also known as cèpes. Have a strong nutty flavour, so only small amounts are required. Must be rehydrated before use.
shiitake when fresh are also known as chinese black, forest or golden oak mushrooms; although cultivated, they have the earthiness and taste of wild mushrooms. Are large and meaty.

swiss brown also called roman or cremini; are light-to-dark brown in colour with a full-bodied flavour.

OIL, GRAPE SEED is a good-quality, neutral vegetable oil pressed from grape seeds.

PAPRIKA a ground dried sweet red capsicum (bell pepper); there are many grades and types available, including sweet, hot, mild and smoked.

PINE NUTS also known as pignoli; not in fact a nut but a small, cream-coloured kernel from pine cones.

PITTA BREAD also known as lebanese bread. This wheat-flour pocket bread is sold in large, flat pieces that separate into two thin rounds. Also available in small thick pieces called pocket pitta.

POMEGRANATE a dark-red, leathery-skinned fruit about the size of an orange filled with hundreds of seeds, each wrapped in an edible lucent-crimson pulp having a tangy sweet-sour flavour. *To remove pomegranate seeds*, cut the pomegranate in half, and use gloved fingers to scrape the seeds from the flesh whilst holding the pomegranate upside down in a bowl of cold water; the seeds will sink and the white pith will float to the surface. Discard the pith, and drain the seeds before using.
pomegranate molasses a thick, tangy syrup made by boiling pomegranate juice into a sticky, syrupy consistency. Available from Middle Eastern food stores, specialty food shops and delis.

POTATO
baby new also known as chats; not a separate variety but an early harvest with very thin skin.
kipfler (fingerling) small, finger-shaped potato with a nutty flavour.

PROSCIUTTO a thinly-sliced Italian, dry-cured ham. Available as crudo (raw) and cotto (cooked).

MAPLE SYRUP a thin syrup distilled from the sap of the maple tree. Maple-flavoured or pancake syrup is not an adequate substitute for the real thing.

QUINOA (keen-wa) is the seed of a leafy plant similar to spinach. It has a delicate, slightly nutty taste and chewy texture. Its cooking qualities are similar to that of rice. You can buy it in most health-food stores; it spoils easily, so keep it sealed in a glass jar under refrigeration. *Quinoa flakes* are rolled and flattened grains.

RADISH, RED a peppery root vegetable related to the mustard plant. The small round red variety is the mildest, it is crisp and juicy, and usually eaten raw in salads.

RHUBARB has thick, celery-like stalks that can reach up to 60cm long; the stalks are the only edible portion of the plant – the leaves contain a toxic substance.

RICE
basmati a white, fragrant long-grained rice. Wash well before cooking.
brown basmati has more fibre and a stronger flavour than white basmati, but it takes twice as long to cook.
microwave milled, cooked then dried rice. Pre-cooked rice is more porous, so that steam can penetrate the grain and rehydrate it in a short time.

RICE NOODLES, DRIED made from rice flour and water, available flat and wide or very thin (vermicelli). Should be soaked in boiling water to soften. Also known as rice stick noodles.

RISONI a small, rice-shaped pasta.

ROLLED OATS oat groats (oats that have been husked) steamed-softened, flattened with rollers, then dried and packaged for consumption as a cereal.

ROSE SYRUP is a boiled mixture of rose petals, sugar and water. Available from Middle-Eastern stores. Not the same as rose essence, which is more concentrated.

SASHIMI GRADE SALMON use the freshest, sashimi-quality fish you can find. Raw fish sold as sashimi has to meet stringent guidelines regarding its handling and treatment after leaving the water. We suggest you seek local advice from authorities before eating any raw seafood.

SAUCE
fish also called nam pla or nuoc nam; made from pulverised fermented fish, most often anchovies. Has a pungent smell and strong taste; use sparingly.
hoisin a thick, sweet and spicy chinese paste made from salted fermented soya beans, onions and garlic.
oyster Asian in origin, this rich, brown sauce is made from oysters and their brine, cooked with salt and soy sauce, and thickened with starches.
soy also known as sieu, is made from fermented soya beans. Several variations are available in most supermarkets and Asian food stores.
sweet chilli a comparatively mild, thai-type sauce made from red chillies, sugar, garlic and vinegar.

SEMOLINA made from durum (hard) wheat milled into textured granules.

SHALLOT also called french shallots, golden shallots or eschalots; small, elongated, brown-skinned members of the onion family. Grows in tight clusters similar to garlic.

SNOW PEAS also called mange tout (eat all). *Snow pea tendrils*, the growing shoots of the plant, are sold by greengrocers. *Snow pea sprouts* tender new growths of snow peas; also known as mange tout.

SUGAR
brown a soft, finely granulated sugar retaining molasses for its characteristic colour and flavour.
caster also known as superfine or finely granulated table sugar.
icing also known as confectioners' sugar or powdered sugar; granulated sugar crushed together with a small amount of added cornflour.
low-GI cane a molasses extract is sprayed onto raw sugar, increasing the time it takes to digest the sugar, resulting in a slower release of energy.

SULTANAS dried grapes, also known as golden raisins.

SUMAC a purple-red, astringent spice ground from berries grown on shrubs that flourish around the Mediterranean; adds a tart, lemony flavour to foods.

TAHINI sesame-seed paste.

TOFU also known as bean curd, an off-white, custard-like product made from the 'milk' of crushed soya beans; comes fresh (soft or firm), or processed (fried or pressed dried sheets). Left over fresh tofu can be refrigerated in water (which is changed daily) for up to 4 days.
silken refers to the method by which it is made – strained through silk.

TOMATOES
roma (egg) also called plum or roma, these are the smallish, oval-shaped tomatoes used in Italian cooking.
truss also known as tiny tim or tom thumb tomatoes; vine-ripened tomatoes with the vine still attached.

TURMERIC a member of the ginger family, its root is dried and ground, resulting in the rich yellow powder that gives many Indian dishes their characteristic colour. It is intensely pungent in taste, but not hot.

VANILLA
bean dried long, thin pod from a tropical golden orchid; the tiny black seeds are used to impart a luscious vanilla flavour.
extract made by pulping chopped vanilla beans with a mixture of alcohol and water. This gives a very strong solution, and only a couple of drops are needed.

VINEGAR
balsamic made from Trebbiano grapes; has a deep rich brown colour with a sweet and sour flavour.
red wine based on fermented red wine.

WASABI an asian horseradish used to make the pungent, green-coloured sauce traditionally served with Japanese raw fish dishes; sold in powdered or paste form.

WEET-BIX oven-roasted wheat-based breakfast biscuit; contains whole wheat grains and barley malt extract.

ZUCCHINI also known as courgette; small green, yellow or white vegetable belonging to the squash family. When harvested young, its edible flowers can be stuffed and deep-fried or baked.

INDEX

Published in 2014 by Bauer Media Books, Sydney
Bauer Media Books is a division of Bauer Media Limited.

MEDIA GROUP

BAUER MEDIA BOOKS
Publisher Jo Runciman
Editorial & food director Pamela Clark
Director of sales, marketing & rights Brian Cearnes
Creative director Hieu Chi Nguyen
Art director & designer Hannah Blackmore
Senior editor Wendy Bryant
Food editor Emma Braz
Contributing writer Sorrel Palmer
Marketing manager Bridget Cody
Senior business analyst Rebecca Varela
Business analyst Ashley Metcalf
Operations manager David Scotto
Production manager Corinne Whitsun-Jones
Circulation manager Nicole Pearson
Published by Bauer Media Books, a division of
Bauer Media Ltd, 54 Park St, Sydney;
GPO Box 4088, Sydney, NSW 2001.
phone (02) 9282 8618; fax (02) 9126 3702

Printed by Toppan Printing Co, China.

Australia Distributed by Network Services,
phone +61 2 9282 8777; fax +61 2 9264 3278;
networkweb@networkservicescompany.com.au
New Zealand Distributed by Netlink Distribution Company,
phone (64 9) 366 9966; ask@ndc.co.nz
South Africa Distributed by PSD Promotions,
phone (27 11) 392 6065/6/7; fax (27 11) 392 6079/80;
orders@psdprom.co.za www.psdpromotions.com

Title: Diabetes/food director, Pamela Clark.
ISBN: 978 174245 434 4 (paperback)
Subjects: Cooking. Diabetes – Diet therapy – Recipes.
Diet in diseases.
Other Authors/Contributors: Clark, Pamela
Dewey Number: 641.56314

© Bauer Media Ltd 2014
ABN 18 053 273 546
Recipe development Jane Howard, Lucy Nunes,
Sharon Kennedy, Jessica Sly
Photographer Louise Lister
Stylist Vivian Walsh
Food preparation Sarah Hobbs, Cynthia Black
Cover Baked apples and raspberries with
quinoa almond crumble, page 108.

To order books
phone 136 116 (within Australia) or
order online at www.awwcookbooks.com.au
Send recipe enquiries to:
recipeenquiries@bauer-media.com.au

Text and recipes checked and endorsed by
The Australian Diabetes Council.

Our latest cookbook

Check out our gorgeous recipes in Cupcakes & Cake Pops

THE AUSTRALIAN **Women's Weekly**
cupcakes & cake pops
Your favourite little cakes have had a glamorous makeover

RRP $12.95

All recipes Triple-Tested in the AWW Test Kitchen to guarantee perfect success every time.

More titles available at selected newsagents & supermarkets or order online now at awwcookbooks.com.au

THE AUSTRALIAN **Women's Weekly**
country classics
wholesome and much-loved recipes from the country table

These wholesome and much-loved recipes bring a little country to the dining table.

THE AUSTRALIAN **Women's Weekly**
fuss-free dinners
Let these supermarket time-savers deliver stress-free meals

These supermarket time-savers will deliver stress-free dinners. Includes mains and desserts.

THE AUSTRALIAN **Women's Weekly**
good food fast
quick, easy, low-fat food to make you feel great

BEST SELLER

Re-released due to popular demand, this best seller is full of quick, easy, low-fat recipes.

THE AUSTRALIAN **Women's Weekly**
food for kids with allergies
Gluten-free, Dairy-free, Egg-free

These gluten, dairy and egg-free recipes are delicious enough for the whole family to enjoy.

THE AUSTRALIAN **Women's Weekly**
cheat's cakes
Buy the cake then decorate it - no-stress birthday cakes for kids

Buy the cake then decorate it; these are the easiest birthday cakes for kids you'll ever make.

THE AUSTRALIAN **Women's Weekly**
monday to friday diet
keep weekend free for fun - an achievable way to lose weight

BREAKFAST • LUNCH • DINNER • SNACKS

Want to enjoy life while losing weight? This diet lets you have weekends off to enjoy yourself.

THE AUSTRALIAN **Women's Weekly**
recipes from around the world

Experience the world on a plate with these much-loved recipes from all corners of the globe.

THE AUSTRALIAN **Women's Weekly**
party food
Substantial to stylish: impressive food to wow your guests

From substantial to stylish: food to wow your guests. Includes menu and party planning tips.